ONE FOR A MAN, TWO FOR A HORSE

ONE FOR A MAN,

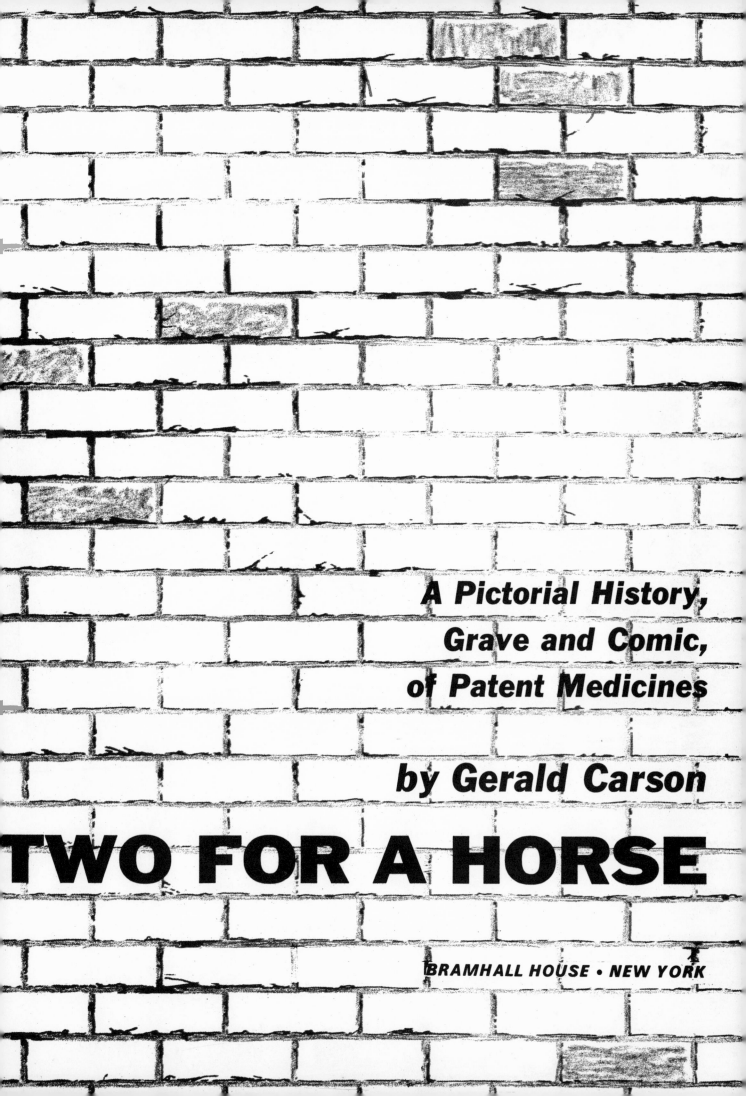

A Pictorial History,
Grave and Comic,
of Patent Medicines

by Gerald Carson

TWO FOR A HORSE

BRAMHALL HOUSE • NEW YORK

Books by Gerald Carson:

THE OLD COUNTRY STORE   CORNFLAKE CRUSADE

THE ROGUISH WORLD OF DOCTOR BRINKLEY   ONE FOR A MAN, TWO FOR A HORSE

HOOD'S SARSAPARILLA

This edition published by Bramhall House,
a division of Clarkson N. Potter, Inc.
a b c d e f g h

Contents

Foreword and Acknowledgments

This book is a souvenir in words and pictures of the "cures" and health devices of long ago, of the picturesque characters who thought them up, the ingenious methods used to sell the merchandise. Once every proper American home had its "doctor book," and a shelf of panaceas whose exact nature was shrouded in secrecy and advertising. The pictures reproduced here have been gathered from widely scattered sources, carefully copied from fragile and fugitive material. They are, it is hoped, entertaining to look at. And they say a good deal about our heritage in such areas as medical history, advertising, publishing and mass distribution, public and private health, social legislation, taste and recreation, and the general level of culture.

Many of today's reputable companies, or their predecessors, advertised their medical goods under the trade-mark of some old *Wunderdoktor*, employing the extravagant advertising tactics of the day.

Self-doctoring should be seen in context. Educated doctors were in short supply. Professional standards were low. It was the day of squabbling systems of medical philosophy—all very confusing to the man who had the pain. There was a legitimate place for simple home remedies for minor ailments.

Formulas, advertising, and ownership of old medicine names mentioned in this chronicle have passed through many transformations. This is the sometimes frightening, sometimes quaint history of the proprietary "cures"—often prescribed for man and beast in varying doses. It is not a commentary upon the social responsibility, business acumen, or moral stature of those who today own trade-marks which may have had in the past a turbulent and checkered history. Nor is the book concerned with the composition or efficacy of any product which exists today under a trade name that is the same as or similar to brand names which may have existed in the nineteenth century or in the early years of the present one.

The sources of pictures are acknowledged on the Picture Credits page. Where no source is recorded, the picture is from the author's collection. For assistance in research, the author gratefully acknowledges

a great obligation to librarians, institutions, and individuals interested in U. S. social history, including the American Antiquarian Society; Oliver Field, Director of the Bureau of Investigation of the American Medical Association, Miss Juelma Williams, and Irwin E. Putzler of the same association; Binghamton Public Library; Buffalo Historical Society; practically the whole staff of the Chicago Historical Society; Harold Titelbaum of the Chicago Public Library; Cleveland Public Library; Miss Sarah Gray, Assistant in the Manuscript Department, Duke University Library; the Federal Trade Commission; Historical Society of Pennsylvania; John Crerar Library; Library of Congress; New York Academy of Medicine; Miss Dorothy C. Barck, editor, *New York History;* Arthur B. Carlson and the reading-room staff, New-York Historical Society; The Newberry Library; New York Public Library; New York State Library; Ohio Historical Society; D. H. Stephens, Chief Inspector, Post Office Department; Texas State Library; University of North Carolina Library; Utica Public Library; the U. S. Trademark Association; and the editor of *The Georgia Review* for permission to reprint material from that magazine in the chapter, "Free Show Tonight."

Also Jacob Blanck, Mr. and Mrs. Edward Brecher, James G. Burrow, Roger Butterfield, Mrs. Albert R. Cauthorn, Alexander Clark, Professor Thomas D. Clark, J. Winston Coleman, Jr.; at Doubleday, William N. Hall, Miss Ruth M. Shair, Ed Kaplin, and so many others who put much of themselves into this book.

I am indebted also to Chester Eisenhuth, Bernard Ellis, Ph.G.; Drs. Morris Fishbein and Jonathan Forman; Mrs. Helen B. Green, George B. Griffenhagen, Mary H. Hebberd, Irving D. Hirsch, Clarence P. Hornung, Frank A. Langdon, Mrs. Berenice Lowe, P. M. McClintock, Arch Merrill, Arthur Miller, William Murrell, Robert Nuese, Tom Parkinson, Daniel R. Pinkham, John W. Ripley, Lawrence B. Romaine, Max Rothstein, Ph. G.; also Allan Sikes, William Spiegler, Mrs. Elleine Stones, Colton Storm, Forest H. Sweet, Lawrence S. Thompson, David Tuffli, Ernest Wessen, Willis Kingsley Wing, W. H. Woodcock, and Professor James Harvey Young.

Before Using.

After Using.

MATERIA PATENT MEDICA

THE DOCTOR'S UNNECESSARY VISIT
HIS PATIENTS BEING CURED BY THE USE OF
DR. TUTT'S LIVER PILLS

Secret remedies, gurgling down the American gullet in a brown, bitter flood, have enjoyed a long and prosperous run as part and parcel of our way of life. Many fine folks have always preferred to do their own medicining. This is the way it was: a man had faith in his watch, his horse, and the patent medicine of his choice.

Before the twentieth century, regular medicine was a sitting duck for the proprietary sharpshooters. It consisted largely of a mixture of trial-and-error "shotgun" medication, tradition, tedious controversies of schools and theorists—and more than a dash of quackery. (Quackery— pretending that one knows more than he does.) Indeed, doctors themselves, from time immemorial, have coined *mots* and epigrams to the general effect that the patients recover in spite of their professional ministrations. The medical literature of the nineteenth century lapsed into generalities when it came to diagnosis and treatment. No such doubts assailed the advertising doctors. They could diagnose and prescribe without even seeing their patient.

Fortunately, the living cell tends to recover—*Natura sanat, non medica,* as Hippocrates saith. But many a patient who had crowded into the stuffy waiting room of a regularly licensed physician had reason to

PHYSICIAN FACTORY

"Avoid the doctors if you value your health" represents one of the gentler propaganda shafts which the proprietary-medicine entrepreneurs directed at the regular physicians. The satiric cartoon above enlarges upon the idea: the regularly licensed doctors are not only incompetent; they are rascals too.

"Dont Speak to me."

All manner of extravagant expressions are possible when a woman's nerves are overwrought.

The spasm at the top of the wind pipe or bronchial tubes, "ball rising in the throat," violent beating of the heart, laughing and crying by turns, muscular spasms (throwing the arms about), frightened by the most insignificant occurrences—are all symptoms of a hysterical condition and serious derangement of the female organs.

Any female complaint may produce hysterics, which must be regarded as a symptom only. The cause, however, yields quickly to **Lydia E. Pinkham's Vegetable Compound,** which acts at once upon the organ afflicted and the nerve centers, dispelling effectually all those distressing symptoms.

Mrs. Lewis Says: "I Feel Like a New Person, Physically and Mentally."

"Dear Mrs. Pinkham:—I wish to speak a good word for Lydia E. Pinkham's Vegetable Compound. For years I had ovarian trouble and suffered everything from nervousness, severe headache, and pain in back and abdomen. I had consulted different physicians, but decided to try your medicine, and I soon found it was giving me much relief. I continued its use and now am feeling like a new person, physically and mentally, and am glad to add one more testimonial to the value of your remedy."— Mrs. M. H. Lewis, 2108 Valentine Ave., Tremont, New York, N. Y.

Writing to Mrs. Pinkham is the quickest and surest way to get the right advice about all female troubles. Her address is Lynn, Mass. She advises women free. Following is an instance:

Mrs. Haven's First Letter to Mrs. Pinkham.

"Dear Mrs. Pinkham:—I would like your advice in regard to my troubles. I suffer every month at time of menstruation, and flow so much and for so long that I become very weak, also get very dizzy. I am troubled with a discharge before and after menses, have pains in ovaries so bad sometimes that I can hardly get around have sore feeling in lower part of bowels, pain in back, bearing-down feeling, a desire to pass urine frequently, with pains in passing it; have leucorrhœa, headache, fainting spells, and sometimes have hysteria. My blood is not in good condition. Hoping to hear from you, I am," Mrs. Emma Haven, 2108 South Ave., Council Bluffs, Iowa. (June 3, 1899.)

Mrs. Haven's Second Letter.

"Dear Mrs. Pinkham:—I wish to express my gratitude for what your medicine has done for me. I suffered for four years with womb trouble. Every month I flowed very badly. I got so bad that I could hardly do my work. Was obliged to sit or lie down the most of the time. I doctored for a long time, but obtained no relief. I began using your remedies—Lydia E. Pinkham's Vegetable Compound, Blood Purifier, Sanative Wash and Liver Pills—and now feel like a new woman."—Mrs. Emma Haven, 2108 South Ave., Council Bluffs, Iowa. (Feb. 1, 1900.)

$5000 REWARD Owing to the fact that some skeptical people have from time to time questioned the genuineness of the testimonial letters we are constantly publishing, we have deposited with the National City Bank, of Lynn, Mass., $5,000, which will be paid to any person who will show that the above testimonials are not genuine, or were published before obtaining the writers' special permission.—Lydia E. Pinkham Medicine Co.

Nurse.—Well, Mrs. Fogy, the Doctor's Ipecac vomits you splendidly. We will soon give you the Calomel and Jalap, next the Castor Oil, then an injection, and after that we will apply the blister and the leeches, and if necessary shave your head. You will be well in three or four weeks,—a little salivated, perhaps, but that's nothing. The Doctor won't charge you more than $40 or $50.

repent his action, echoing the sentiments of the disgruntled patient who wrote, "I wish now I would have stayed home from Omaha." It was under these circumstances that a man would turn to a course of Wahoo Bitters.

What with results so chancy, the medics quarreling fiercely among themselves, the pepper-and-steam doctors arrayed against the homeopathic, eclectic, botanic, and bleeding-and-calomel schools, and a house call costing a whole dollar, it is not surprising that the doctor was often summoned only when the patient was *in extremis*—by the same lad who went to get the minister. The patient who turned to ready-made medicines read the circular wrapped around the bottle and felt a renewal of his symptoms and his faith. He did not know or much care what was in the bottle. The purchase depended upon the effect, real or imagined.

The case against the proprietaries was that they induced the ignorant to treat themselves for serious diseases and syndromes and that they contained secret and often dangerous drugs, including narcotics, which could make the victim feel high as a junky. The industry's advertising became a national scandal for its unabashed untruthfulness. Eventually the efforts of the federal government to save the people from their folly resulted in the Food and Drugs Act of 1906, a pioneer statute which contained some notable omissions and jokers. Nevertheless, it was a good law, later

THE NEW WAY OF CURING THE SICK.

Husband.—*What, Mary, well already, and eating toast and tea! I left you with a raging fever this morning.*
Wife.—*Yes, Albert, I am well already, and I took nothing but six of Spence's Positive Powders. They acted like a charm, and they cost only two cents and a half a piece. That is the tiniest doctor's bill you ever paid.*

"John, I just wish you would taste this bottle of Cough Syrup."

amended, broadened, and strengthened. It placed some restraint, at least, upon the wheeling and dealing of the nostrum peddlers who taught their rustic customers, in a significant old phrase, to "light one bottle on another."

All honor should go to the magazines and newspapers who refused the advertisements of charlatans and un-mitigated liars. Also to George (Pop) Stansfield, a Topeka, Kansas, druggist. During the first decade of this century, Pop amazed his clientele and received nationwide attention by hanging a large sign in his store, "We sell patent medicines but do not recommend them."

Speaking precisely, there is no such thing in the United States as a patent medicine. The term is a misnomer, but deeply rooted in history. The kings of England have for centuries granted "patents of royal favor" to the bootmaker, tailor, and mediciner who served the royal family. The first American colonists, as loyal Englishmen, esteemed the medicines which bore the token of royal favor—the "patents." Hence the term, which has nothing whatever to do with the United States Patent Office. The latter requires the full disclosure of an invention, and that it be new and useful. The last thing the businessman of medicine had in mind was disclosure of his formula. He would also know that in most cases it would be immediately recognized as being either dangerous or at least charmingly unoriginal. The *vis medicatrix*—efficacy—of the remedies lay in their mystique.

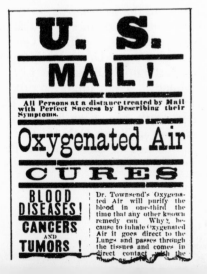

Count Your Symptoms ...Is One Missing?

To that proportion of the population who at any given time were genuinely in need of medical attention must be added a veritable Garden of Eden begging for cultivation —those who were seized with fancies of ill health, who felt their pulses, looked at their tongues every morning, and counted their symptoms each day to see if one were missing. From the medical regulars, such patients often got short shrift. But the advertising doctors practiced psychosomatic medicine long before the term had been invented. They stepped in with symptoms, sympathy, and concern. Why is your liver torpid? Do you have a loved one whose sands of life are ebbing fast? Read how Dr. Brown's pill removed a wen—read and reflect. A granger, let us say, was off his feed. He took a swig of medicine. In a day or so he felt fine, as he should have in any case. Nature did the work, but the pink pills got the credit. "If you got empathy," as Peter Lind Hayes, the well-known entertainer, has said, "you got it made."

They were secrets or nostrums, meaning, literally, "ours." What the gentlemen of the proprietaries were interested in was not patents but coined trade names, such as Dr. Adams' Wart Cure, Dent's Toothache Gum, or Kellogg's Safe Fat Reducer, registered with the U.S. patent office as a *trade name,* indicating the brand, not the product, and capable of a stout defense under our trade-mark laws.

Commercially, patent medicines had these attractions: they were light in weight, slight in bulk, high in value—an ideal combination in an age of poor transportation. The aura of the brand name gave the article qualities of a monopoly. When most people could read—a little—and believed in the truth of an ad for Kennedy's Pasture Weed, printed by letterpress, the same as the Holy Bible, the profits that could be made out of the true believers were awesome. Dr. James

Caleb Jackson of Dansville, New York, reported after only a few years' practice that he knew a man who had taken sixty-four boxes of Brandreth's Pills and over nine hundred patients to his knowledge had downed from three to fifteen bottles of Townsend's Sarsaparilla. At the time, 1857, there were over fifteen hundred patents being advertised in the newspapers.

Among the early patent medicines of British origin were Anderson's Scots Pills, Godfrey's Cordial, Dr. Bateman's Pectoral Drops, Dr. John Hooper's Female Pills, Robt. Turlington's Balsam of Life, "a Remedy for every Malady." These imported proprietaries moved west with the trader and emigrant; fragments of a Turlington bottle have been found on the site of an old trading post in North Dakota. The first medical pamphlet published in New York, a Peter Zenger imprint devoted to extolling the virtues of Dr.

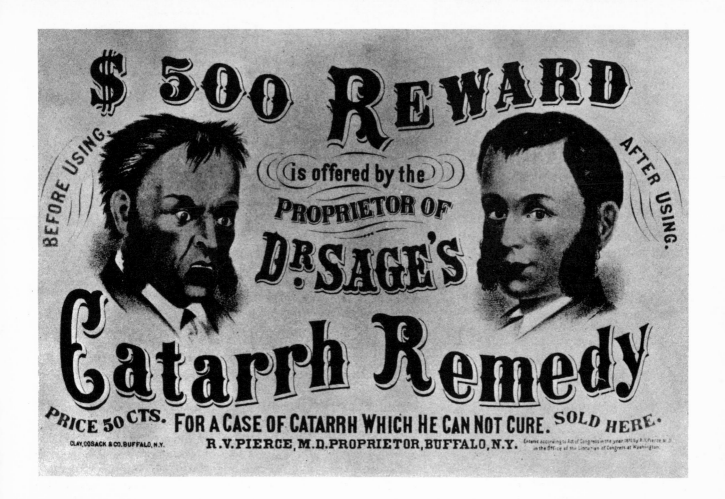

Bateman's Pectoral Drops, has been suggested by Mr. Lawrence B. Romaine, the leading authority on the American trade catalogue, as being "the first American printed catalog." The drops cured, incidentally, gout, rheumatism, jaundice, stone, asthma, colds, rickets, and melancholy. Soon the enterprising Yankees were importing English bottles and filling them with American draughts, then moved on from imitation to deceptions of their own devising. These were usually bark-and-root formulas copied out of pharmacopoeias and old herbals:

> "Trefoil, vervain, John's wort, dill,
> Hinders witches of their will."

Many of the packaged medicines had their background in old folk cures. Every mountain cove, every fork of the creek, had an old aunt, granny, notions peddler, or visiting Indian who treated the inhabitants with decoctions, infusions, tinctures, etc., made from dried specimens gathered from forest, field, and stream bank. The prestige of granny medicine is remarkably durable. At present writing, a book on folk medicine reigns at the top of the best-seller lists. Myths and prejudices, primitive notions, provided the basis for what might be called materia *patent* medica—sour-dock ointment for the itch, mullein for the bowels, and the "doctrine of the signatures" for philosophy. This was derived from the idea that some particular plant was a specific for every disease, and that one could tell which ailment a plant would cure by a mark on the

11

plant. Usually a slug of senna, cascara, or aloes was shot into the herb medicine. "The mixture was a darned good physic," one patent-medicine operative has said defensively, "and the natives got their money's worth." A physic seems to have been what everybody needed, judging by the warm regard in which the populace held their packaged medicines.

Confidence was built by testimonials and "reward offers." The latter were quite safe to make. The Liquozone Company offered $1000 for any germ that Liquozone wouldn't kill—no restrictions as to whether one froze him or boiled him. Hall's Catarrh Cure had a $100 guarantee. One man took twenty-six bottles, then asked for his money back. But that was an easy one for the Hall's people. He hadn't given this meritorious product a fair trial.

The ready-made medicines may be classified generally as single-purpose or all-purpose. It might seem that the single-purpose remedy was missing a lot of bets. But not so. Catarrh, for example, was a great catchword. Every ailment was catarrh in the palmy days of Munyon's Catarrh Tablets (baking soda, borax, common salt, possibly a trace of carbolic acid). Peddlers of nostrums did not need extensive medical or pharmacal knowledge. In fact, it may well have been a handicap to the free play of the imagination so necessary in that field of endeavor. The game was to hit on some name that would catch the public fancy, possibly through alliteration, as with Burdock's Blood Bitters, or Radway's Ready Relief. And so successful were the medicine men at finding the winning combination that by 1914 there were 3085 establishments in the United States turning out goods worth $105,665,611 at wholesale.

Although he called upon Aesculapius and his daughter, Panacea, the owner of a laxative or wart

remover was actually a businessman, concerned with trade-marks, newspaper circulations and rates, screw-neck bottles, capping machines, the cost of smothering Berkeley, California, with samples, or Washington, D.C., with tack signs. And the medicine packager was especially interested in scoundrels who tried to muscle in. New York had two Dr. Townsends; Philadelphia sheltered a Dr. Swayne and a Dr. Swaim. Dr. McLean, out in St. Louis, armed the good people against the substituting druggist. When the retailer tries such a trick, the doctor warned, "Look at him, and you will see *Penitentiary* written in his countenance. That is his destiny; sooner or later."

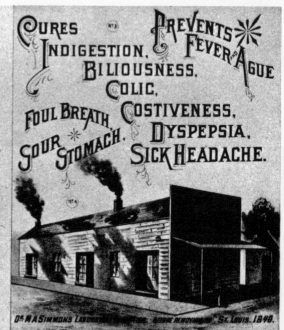

Many a hawker who later made his pile got his start on the roads and byways as a vendor of dried herbs, then graduated to packaged medicines. Nathaniel Hawthorne remembered a chance meeting with such a man, a Dr. Jacques, "sensible in his talk—but not a gentleman . . . a simplicity about him that is likeable, though I believe he comes from Philadelphia."

"AND HER GOLDEN HAIR WAS HANGING DOWN HER BACK"

In the spacious days of William B. McKinley, the dollar watch, and the three-dollar shoe, the seven Sutherland sisters came upon the town with a preparation which they sold by demonstrating their own luxuriant locks. Sara, Victoria, Mary, Dora, Isabella, Grace, and Naomi not only had the longest, thickest hair ever seen in Niagara County, New York, where they hailed from—they had THE LONGEST HAIR IN THE WORLD. Their hair and their tonic transformed them into fairy princesses swathed in furs, dripping with diamonds.

The Sutherland tresses were brown, not golden, as in the old song, but they were hanging down the girls' backs, all right. When, during their musical act in the Barnum and Bailey show, they did a reverse and all presented their *derrières* to the spectators, the combined length of crowning glory was thirty-six feet, ten inches. The sisters were all big, strong farm girls, not ravishing beauties, but handsome enough. They could sing a little and play a little, and they got by all right,

THE WORLD-RENOWNED SEVEN SUTHERLAND SISTERS

"It's the Hair – Not the Hat"

first at church socials and local doings, later in store windows and with the circus. But it was their cascading hair and their hair medicine that made the Sutherland name a household word.

The father, Fletcher Sutherland, was a poor farmer, born with the gift of gab. He practiced law without a license, did some preaching without apostolic blessing, and called himself Reverend. Fletcher got up the hair grower, exhibited the daughters, got

the thing off the ground, and died. Thereafter the girls enjoyed three golden decades. And "enjoyed" is the right word. As one old resident who knew the sisters clear back to the Warren's Corners days said, "When they had it, they spent it."

The septet were impulsive, impractical, and full of whimsies. They built a mansion on the old home place, near Lockport, New York, peaked with gables and turrets, filled with marble bathrooms, three furnaces, a life-sized oil painting of the seven sisters on the living-room wall, an attic filled with Saratoga trunks. There was a gazebo on the lawn, around which the sisters rode their high wheelers, wearing scanty bathing suits, their precious locks covered with cloth masks to protect them from the sun.

The eccentricities of the Sutherland sisters were the talk of the Western New York fruit belt. Sara had seventeen cats and a horse which was shod with gold-plated shoes. One sister had a dog which rang a bell when he wanted service. On tour, the girls were accompanied by seven maids to comb their hair, and seven dolls three feet tall, each doll equipped with a head of its owner's hair. The girls filled out their treatment line with a scalp cleaner, shampoo, and hair dye. But the hair grower was the wheel horse. They never let their hair down as to what was in the square, panel bottle with their name blown into the glass. Some folks up Lockport way say it was a mixture of rain water and alcohol, with some coloring matter added. The state Board of Health of New Hampshire pretty much agreed, after running some tests. When Frederick H. Castlemaine, the rakehell husband of Isabella, repaired to Dan Rodenbeck's saloon in the old Hodge Opera House block in Lockport, he would order drinks for the house, with a side remark, "Just another bottle of hair tonic."

Bobbed hair, after World War I, and the ways of a fool with his money, finally dammed up the golden flood. Grace, the last of the sisters, died in 1946—stone broke.

In crinoline days, two ladies could—at least in an advertisement—carry on a discussion of super-fluous hair, as follows:

EMILY: Good morning, my dear Cousin, what in the world are you doing?

SUSAN: I am delighted to see you, Emily; you know my great affliction and have often sympathized with me on account of the growth of hair on my upper lip, arms and neck, which rendered my appearance so masculine. You will now rejoice with me in the dis-

Long before Rheingold, the well-known New York beer, hit upon the happy idea of choosing by popular vote a nubile Rhine maiden each year to promote its brew, Dr. J. C. Ayer, of Lowell, Massachusetts, called upon the German legend of the Lorelei to lend a helping hand, or fin, to his Hair Vigor. Note that the shipwrecked sailors are Americans, flying the Stars and Stripes in the distress position—upside down.

EVERY WOMAN CAN BE BEAUTIFUL.

Superfluous Hair Destroyed Forever by a Wonderful Electrical Invention—Without Pain—Without Injury—Without Expense. A Godsend to Every Tortured Woman.

covery which I made one month since, of an article capable of removing the Hair and destroying the roots. This is the very precious compound with which I have removed the Hair and Roots from my upper lip and neck, and I am now engaged in removing it from my arm.

EMILY: It is certainly a great discovery. I am not distressed as you have been, but the Hair, you know, is too low-seated on my forehead, which gives me a stupid and unfavorable appearance; do you think my dear cousin that the compound will remove it?

SUSAN: It will remove the thickest beard of a man, each application will make the Hair grow thinner, and at last the roots will be destroyed.

EMILY: Where can that article be found? I will not wait a minute.

SUSAN: You will find it at Jules Hauel's Wholesale and Retail Perfumery Store, No. 46 South Third Street, below Chestnut, Philadelphia, *where it is prepared* . . .

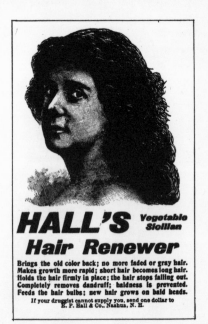

"Natural Waists or No Wives"

Here is Lysistrata in reverse—the threat that young men will not choose life partners who practice tight lacing. The pitch here is not for a medicine or a gadget but a 12½-cent lecture. But the subject is still delicate health, with the "Galloping Consumption" hovering offstage.

16

"OH-H-H, we'll sing of Lydia Pinkham...

There was a theory widely held during the last century that women were normally in a delicate condition, and that in some way not clearly explained their round of suffering was caused by the perfidy and brutality of men. Lady novelists worked the theme hard. Patent medicines catering to the female-weakness market extended sympathy, advice, and a jug of bitters to the unhappy victims of hot flashes, prolapsed uteri, and the symptoms directly associated with the calendar.

Perhaps the most colorful promotional methods of the last seventy-five years are associated with the prim Victorian lady whose photograph appears above

—grave, composed, in her best black silk with a bit of ruching at the neck, competent, warmhearted, crusading Mrs. Lydia E. Pinkham, of Lynn, Massachusetts, trustworthy, homey, sadly sweet—what a woman! Or, what a photograph! "Only a woman," said Mrs. Pinkham, "can understand a woman's ills." Lydia E. Pinkham became a master of teakettle medicine and grandmother of modern advertising.

Although Mrs. Pinkham died in 1883, rich, respected, an enthusiastic member of the W.C.T.U., her greatest fame was posthumous. Twenty years or so ago, it was estimated that some $40,000,000 had been spent in publishing her picture. Country editors, well

...and her love for the human race..."

supplied with advertising cuts of Lydia, once the only portrait of a lady to be found in country print shops, often ran Lydia's face as Dr. Mary Walker, the lady who wore trousers, President Cleveland's bride, Sarah Bernhardt, or Queen Victoria. Lithographs of the famous portrait study were distributed to the drugstores, smaller cards to their customers. Lydia's likenesses, with that cast-iron smile, went on souvenir plates and gift items. There were Pinkham jokes and editorial wisecracks, and Bill Nye, the humorist, nominated Mrs. P. for President. College boys, using feminine pseudonymns, wrote to Lydia for advice on timidity, frigidity, and similar intimate matters. At stag dinners, in fraternity houses, they sang to the tune of the old hymn, "I Will Sing of My Redeemer":

> Mrs. Jones of Walla Walla,
> Mrs. Smith from Kankakee,
> Mrs. Cohn, Mrs. Murphy,
> Sing your praises lustily.

> REFRAIN: OH-H-H, we'll sing of Lydia Pinkham,
> And her love for the human race.
> How she sells her vegetable compound,
> And the papers, the papers they publish,
>   they publish her FACE!

There were many versions of the Pinkham balladry. Some could only appear in a volume of curiosa printed for private circulation, for shipment by express.

At one time Lydia's son, Dan, toyed with the idea that the compound should be for both sexes. But Lydia gently vetoed that gambit. Nevertheless, the compound was so good that drug clerks in dry Kansas used to report that many male customers bought the medication to ward off chills, snakebite, and fallen uterus. Dan was the idea man, the promotional genius of the Pinkham clan. One of his ideas, which worked out very well, was to drop personal notes, which appeared to have been accidently lost, in cemeteries just before the Memorial Day crowds arrived. The notes all spoke highly, and urgently, of the vegetable compound.

Lydia Estes Pinkham was born in Lynn, February 9, 1819, the daughter of a shoemaker. Educated in the local academy, she was caught up in the reform spirit of her times—Swedenborgianism, phrenology, temperance, the dietary doctrines of Sylvester Graham, women's rights, spiritualism, and fiat money. There must have been something special in the air of Lynn, which knew also such other remarkable women as Susan B. Anthony, Mrs. Mary Sargeant Neal Gove Nichols, and Mary Baker Eddy.

Lydia married Pinkham in 1843, reared a family, did some nursing, and late in life produced the famous herb remedy, using a recipe her husband had received from a machinist named Todd as part settlement on an old debt. The vegetable compound made its commercial debut in 1875, at a time when the family faced actual hunger. The children filled bottles and folded circulars. Mother Pinkham slaved over a hot stove, whipping up the medicine, pausing to give counsel on merchandising and distribution, while with the other hand, so to speak, she wrote intimate and emotional handbills stressing the beneficence of the word "vegetable."

The vegetable compound was once advertised as a "cure" for "all FEMALE WEAKNESS," spelled out in explicit detail. The version of the package shown (below) disclosing the alcoholic content and saying that the medicine is simply "for" falling of the womb, etc., appeared after medicine labels were toned down by the federal Food and Drugs Act. Today, the compound is still going strong, paced by a companion product, Lydia E. Pinkham's Tablets, especially made for the woman who "Can't Give Your Husband Real Companionship."

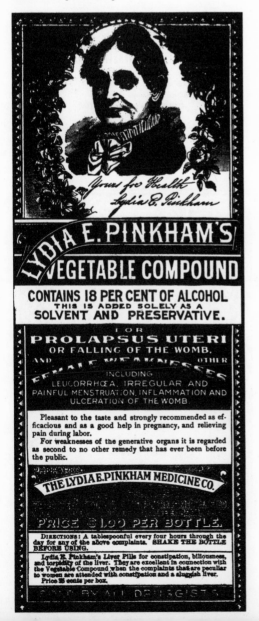

19

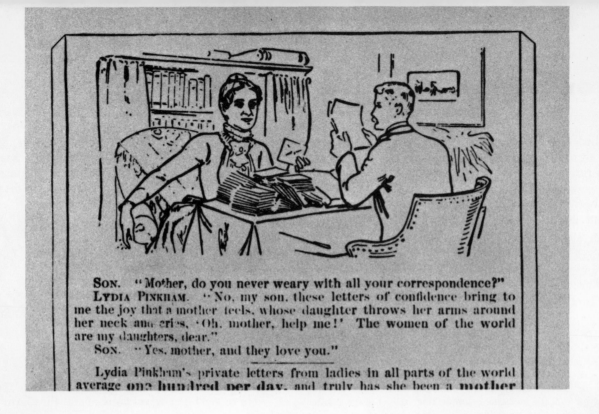

SON. "Mother, do you never weary with all your correspondence?"
LYDIA PINKHAM. "No, my son, these letters of confidence bring to me the joy that a mother feels, whose daughter throws her arms around her neck and cries, 'Oh, mother, help me!' The women of the world are my daughters, dear."
SON. "Yes, mother, and they love you."

Lydia Pinkham's private letters from ladies in all parts of the world average one hundred per day, and truly has she been a mother

Pinkham advertising copy always ended with an invitation to weak women to lay their troubles on Mrs. Pinkham's strong shoulders. And long after Lydia had been gathered to her fathers, the Pinkham concern encouraged maladjusted women to write to "Mrs. Pinkham." They had one too, in case anyone was interested—Lydia's daughter-in-law, Mrs. Charles Pinkham. Elbert Hubbard and other biographers, the lusty songs, the national sense of humor, the company's ads, which kept Lydia's spirit marching on, have all combined to perpetuate the name of a shrewd and plucky New England woman who was engaged in the manufacture of patent medicine for only the last eight years of her life.

NOW RAISES
600 CHICKENS

After Being Relieved of Organic Trouble by Lydia E. Pinkham's Vegetable Compound.

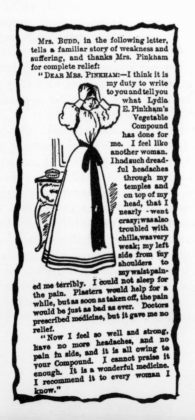

Mrs. BUDD, in the following letter, tells a familiar story of weakness and suffering, and thanks Mrs. Pinkham for complete relief:

"DEAR MRS. PINKHAM:—I think it is my duty to write to you and tell you what Lydia E. Pinkham's Vegetable Compound has done for me. I feel like another woman. I had such dreadful headaches through my temples and on top of my head, that I nearly went crazy; was also troubled with chills, was very weak; my left side from my shoulders to my waist pained me terribly. I could not sleep for the pain. Plasters would help for a while, but as soon as taken off, the pain would be just as bad as ever. Doctors prescribed medicine, but it gave me no relief.

"Now I feel so well and strong, have no more headaches, and no pain in side, and it is all owing to your Compound. I cannot praise it enough. It is a wonderful medicine. I recommend it to every woman I know."

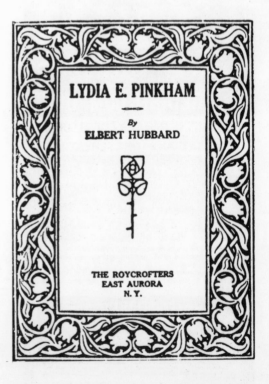

LYDIA E. PINKHAM

By
ELBERT HUBBARD

THE ROYCROFTERS
EAST AURORA
N.Y.

The incidence of rheumatism, dyspepsia, typhoid fever, tuberculosis, the hazards of childbirth—all indicate that the level of public health in pioneer America was low, and that women *did* have perils "peculiar to their sex." Small wonder that they took laudanum, nipped at alcoholic tonics, and read the novels of Susan Warner and Mary J. Holmes, which presented ill health as a secret weapon in the war between the men and the women. Mrs. Pinkham's Vegetable Compound didn't work this street without competition. Dr. Kilmer's Swamp Root was in there pitching too, and Tanlac, and Thedford's Black Draught, and Wine of Cardui, which contained, in addition to the "necessary preservative," a formula employing golden seal, black haw, and blessed thistle, and enjoyed such confidence that Southern ladies frequently took the remedy direct from the bottle.

Thousands of Women Have Kidney Trouble and Never Suspect It.

WINE OF CARDUI

The Reverend R. L. McElree, who preached the theology of Cumberland Presbyterianism, was pastor of a little flock at Fayetteville, Tennessee. McElree's opportunity for larger service came when his attention was called to some herbs, along with a circumstantial story of how they came into the family of a parishioner from an old Indian squaw. The reverend promptly went into the patent-medicine business as the creator of Wine of Cardui, "Nature's Great Emmenagogue," with a wrapper illustrated by the picture of a plant, an Indian maiden, an ill woman, and the legend: "The Great Spirit planted it, take and be healed." In good time, Cardui and Black Draught stood forth together in black and yellow paint on just about every barn and shed in Dixie—universal symbol of recovery in the New South.

DID NOT HAVE STRENGTH TO COMB HER HAIR

"Since taking Tanlac I look and feel like a different person," recently asserted Mrs. Lewis Herbolzhiemer, 40 Portland St., Worcester, Mass.

"Two years of stomach trouble brought on a complication of ills that were fast shattering my health. Indigestion kept me in constant pain and misery and I actually did not have strength to comb my hair. My nerves were so excited that I would wake up all hours of the night and loss of sleep was just wearing me out.

"As badly run down as I was it has only taken six bottles of Tanlac to make me feel like my normal self. My troubles are not only gone, but I eat and sleep like a child and have gained twenty pounds. My gratitude to Tanlac is unbounded."

Tanlac is for sale by all good druggists. Accept no substitute. Over 40 million bottles sold.

Tanlac Vegetable Pills, for constipation, made and recommended by the manufacturers of TANLAC.—Advt.

21

Straight Talk to Women

The cult of bigness in the area of secondary-sex characteristics created the bust-line racket: the desire called forth the devices. In our time it has been hormone creams, exercise equipment involving coil springs and rubber loops, cone-shaped falsies, pills, and mail-order "bosom beauty" courses. But there is nothing new about all this. "Graceful plumpness," as Egyptian Regulator Tea pointed out long ago, "is ever the admiration of the opposite sex." Plain-looking, flat-chested ladies in need of restorative action were assured that this great and never-failing brew was used by the Empress Eugénie, Lady Mordaunt (Edward VII was named as corespondent in the great Mordaunt scandal), and the "society beauties" of the United States.

Will You Try the Tea for Bustline Beauty...

Before Treatment. After Using Two Weeks. After Using Four Weeks. After Using Two Months.

Egyptian Regulator Tea said it gave Mabel Gray, "the beautiful but frail courtesan" of London, vibrant bust beauty, and promised the interested public an enlargement of from two to six inches in the appropriate places. The tea was also sold as a freckle-remover. It was a physic.

...or the Spanish System at the Old $10 Price?

Dr. Harmon agreed to make curvaceous Spanish *señoritas* out of his correspondents by a home treatment worth $150 (his estimate) but which he sold on a special last-chance basis for $10 to every woman who would inveigle a friend into signing up for the course. There are few "hooks" used in modern advertising which this San Francisco doc didn't understand and use.

Before Treatment. After Using One-Third of Course. After Using Two-Thirds of Course. After Using Full Course.

Despite the promise held forth in the ad (left), skeptics insisted lyrically that there were limits to the sorcery of even the most gifted advertising doctor: "There's a baby in every bottle,/So the old quotation ran./But the Federal Trade Commission/Still insists you'll need a man." Pregnant married ladies were warned to avoid the French Pills, as they invariably caused a miscarriage.

INDIAN CURES

For some two hundred and fifty years, the American settlers despised and feared the American Indian. Yet, at the same time, the Indian was a stock figure for elegaic treatment in romantic literature, including patent-medicine literature. The ads for Indian remedies praised the nobility of the red man, his eloquence, his remarkably good health, and his medicines. The belief in botanic medicine and a primitive hostility toward the educated doctor—both flowed together and climaxed in the belief that untutored peoples were "natural" physicians. The Noble Savage was, as the *Kickapoo Almanac* (1896) pointed out, "A better curative agent than the youth who, after a dozen medical lectures or so"—as the writers with a certain animus against organized medicine put it—"is given

authority as an M.D. to try his hand on anybody that comes along."

The argument was that, in the growing things of the earth, nature provides the means of overcoming disease, as she provides the means of shelter, food, and so forth. Dr. John Goodale Briante, who was for many years with the St. Francis Indians at Green Bay, was a do-it-yourself doctor—didn't even believe in the patents. So he compiled a book for the housewife to use, revealing various Indian secrets: how to make your own liniment out of skunk's oil, to de-worm the children with sweet fern. Briante scorned "Quack Doctors and Patent Medicines," who have found that "it is easier to cheat a man out of his life, than out of a dollar." But, one wonders, why not both?

Little Bright Eyes

This Indian Venus symbolized the curative powers of Prairie Plant as used by the squaws of Indian Territory and packaged by a couple of light-hearted philanthropists in New Haven, Connecticut. The princess existed, alas, only in Kickapoo advertising circulars.

23

Back in colonial times the Indians of Georgia no doubt sent out smoke signals to let the other Indians know they had a good medicine. Now the S.S.S. folks of Atlanta, who own the old Indian formula, send out heap powerful radio signals.

Here the Indian-medicine routine gets a new twist. In the woodcut below, the Osage Indians dance out their thanks to "Prof. Fritz," a Chicago patent-medicine man, who discovered a miraculous herb all by himself that cured them of the galloping consumption. The doctor is sitting on the rock, left, downstage, watching the choreography.

The whole concept of Indian pharmacology was blown up to ridiculous proportions. Francis Parkman, the historian, who had lived among the Sioux, says that the Indians had many simple applications for wounds, aimed more at placating supernatural influences than at curing disease. It took the white man's commercial instincts and luxuriant imagination to embroider the campfire tales of remarkable cures produced by Indian shamen.

For instance, as an example of this genre, it is recounted that there was a Dr. Cunard, a skilled botanist, who joined up with an old "mountain man" named Dubois at St. Louis to study the medicinal flora of the Rockies. Dr. Cunard lived with the Indians —home was where he hung his hat. Once, over the border in Mexico—it was Navajo country—Cunard saw the Indians gather around a stake and prepare the fire. Horrors! They were about to burn a maiden of faultless beauty. Her name was, it turned out later, Tula. What brought Tula to the stake was a melodramatic proposition: Marry the chief or die.

"Dog of a Navajo," Tula answered, "I defy thee. I am the daughter of an Aztec chief. The Eagle mates not with the thieving hawk."

Are you ahead of me? Yes, the white doctor saved Tula by the clever strategem of predicting an eclipse which convinced the Indians that they had better unhand the maid. Cunard knew about the eclipse, you see, because he had been studying his almanac, probably the one put out by B. L. Judson & Company, which manufactured the Mountain Herb Pills. Their formula was Dr. Cunard's reward for saving the Indian princess.

The Osage Indians holding a pow-wow, or dance, as thanks to the Great Spirit for the discovery of the herb, *Mas-e-ar-ve-wat-char*, by Prof. Fritz, used among them for the cure of Consumption, with great success, branches of which they are seen holding aloft while performing the ceremony. WHITE HAIR, THE CHIEF, is seen with a star on his breast, and WENGA-SHEE, the Great Medicine Man, with an oval ornament of curious design, supposed to act as a charm to shield him from harm in time of battle. The Doctor (with his servant and dog) is seen sitting on a rock, to the left, witnessing the ceremony.

Although this compound was sold for coughs and colds, it was often used when the family diagnosis suggested the theory, "Maybe it was something you ate." Custom called for the prompt resort to an infusion or decoction of boneset (*Eupatorium perfoliatum*), which would cause the patient to upchuck.

This busy brave types the medicine man who used to visit county-seat towns of the South and Midwest on court days. The chief would put on a hard-driving pitch for his panacea, especially snake oil, which he guaranteed would cure everything from toothache to toeache. Here he is shown crying his wares on the public square in Morehead, Kentucky, county seat of Rowan County.

The demure maid watering her child's garden of herbs provided Dr. Morse with exactly the image he desired for his pills. When entertainment was limited to an occasional taffy pull or game of Copenhagen, such advertisements brought a bit of cheer into the lives of families that seldom saw a picture of any kind.

Dr. MORSE'S INDIAN ROOT PILLS

W. H. COMSTOCK, *Sole Proprietor,*
MORRISTOWN, N.Y.

An old chief who used to live on the Umatilla Reservation, sold Ka-ton-Ka (lower right) on street corners along with a book about himself entitled *Daring Donald McKay, or, The Last War Trail of the Modocs,* which ran through many editions. The book, sponsored by Ka-ton-Ka, asked rhetorically, Who ever saw a bald Indian? Who ever saw an Indian with bad teeth? Who ever saw an Indian with a deranged liver? (Who, indeed, ever saw an Indian?) The red men know nothing of drugstores with their doctor jargon and prescription Latin. They just take good old Ka-ton-Ka freely and live to be a hundred.

26

"The Leaves of the Forest were for the Healing of the Nation"

KA-TON-KA

Is Nature's GIFT to Nature's Children

Seek Ye the ROOT and the BRANCH, they are LIFE Giving and LIFE Preserving.

We refer you to pages 1085, 1752, 1423, 843, 1250, 423, 402, 859, 422, 182 in the U. S. DISPENSATORY, fifteenth edition, 1887, the highest standard authority on Materia Medica, and see what is said about these roots, herbs and barks which, with others, are used in the best Medicine on Earth.

Health is Perishable as well as Attainable.
Good Health is never Appreciated until it is Gone.

KA-TON-KA
CURES
OR PAYS BACK THE MONEY.

Pure Air, Pure Water, Pure Food, Pure Skin
are the four cardinal principles in preserving health. To restore health is another thing and involves the healthy action of the four great Organs of the body,

STOMACH, LIVER, KIDNEYS AND BLOOD

Ka-ton-Ka is Guaranteed & Secured by Bond
TO ★ CURE ★ OR ★ REFUND ★ THE ★ MONEY.

A BANK DRAFT WITH EVERY BOTTLE I SELL

Col. T. A. Edwards First introduced Medicines obtained from Indians in 1876, since that time many imitators have placed Medicines on the Market claiming them to be of Indian origin, but none of these imitators with their substitutes can guarantee cures. The Oregon Indian Medicine Co. puts up BANKABLE PAPER to Guarantee their Goods.

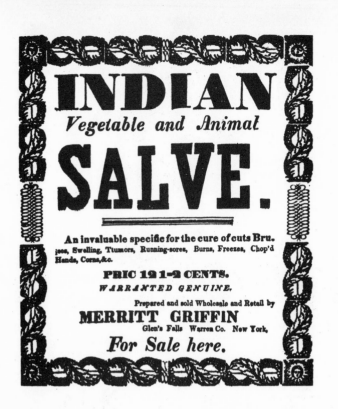

INDIAN
Vegetable and Animal
SALVE.

An invaluable specific for the cure of cuts Bru.
ises, Swelling, Ttumors, Running-sores, Burns, Freezes, Chop'd
Hands, Corns,&c.

PRIC 12 1-2 CENTS.
WARRANTED GENUINE,

Prepared and sold Wholesale and Retail by

MERRITT GRIFFIN
Glen's Falls Warren Co. New York,

For Sale here.

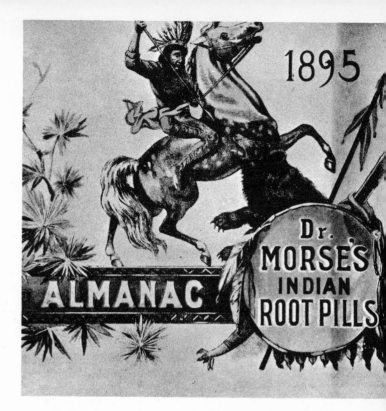

1895

ALMANAC

Dr. MORSE'S INDIAN ROOT PILLS

DR. NEWALL,
THE NATIVE
INDIAN DOCTOR,

Most respectfully offers his services in the Original Indian Healing Art, to the sick and afflicted in this vicinity. Dr. Newell may be consulted at the Indian Encampment in this place,
Where he will remain for a short time and furnish those in want of Medicine enough to cure them.

Dr. N.'s healing skill is original, having come down from many generations. Should Physicians speak evil of the Doctor's practice, pay no attention to what they say, for in so doing they speak evil of what they do not understand. What does the white man know of the Original Indian practice as it existed 400 years ago, and as it now exists ! They know but little.

Dr. N. thinks that there are many good Doctors among his white friends, but does not believe they cure all diseases as they pretend. He does not pretend to cure all diseases, but can cure many. The Great Spirit is kind—he has taught his creatures to know what is good for them.— The real Natives of America have learned many good Medicines from the Beasts, Fowls, Fishes, and even from the insignificant Insects themselves.

Dr. Newall has Medicines for the under-mentioned diseases, viz :

COSTIVENESS, INDIGESTION, DYSPEPSIA, FLATULENCY, HEADACHE,
Cold Stomach, Cough, Pain in the Stomach, Jaundice, Dropsy, Stranguary, &c.

In all diseases Incident to Females, in particular, the superior efficacy of Dr. Newell's Medicines has been long tested and highly appreciated.

DIRECTIONS FOR USE WILL BE GIVEN WITH THE MEDICINES.

A white Doctor says that his Medicines made from one Root cure all diseases, but **Dr. Newall** does not believe it, for there are many white Doctors who say they learnt from the Indian Doctors the art of doctoring in the Indian way, when in fact they know nothing about it. They advertise largely what they can do, and put on the Indian name : but when called upon for a trial, it is found they are very different from the genuine Indian Doctor, and that their seeming knowledge is nothing but false pretension.

During the dark days of the Revolutionary War—so the story goes—in Ulster County, New York, lived a family named Masten, devoted to the American cause. Mrs. Betsy Masten, a great favorite with the Mohawks and the soldiers suffering from the ravages of camp life, had a great reputation for her cough medicine. But she was no hand at all with running sores, cutaneous diseases, or piles. One day while Mrs. Masten was at her spinning wheel, a shadow darkened her door. It was the aged squaw, Ke-ne-o-ta. The following colloquy took place:

"Why, Ke-ne-o-ta, why are you here?"

"Me tired, me hungry."

Mrs. Masten refreshed the Mohawk, when Ke-ne-o-ta said suddenly, "You no sleep good."

"Why, Ke-ne-o-ta, how do you know this? No one knows my thoughts."

"Me had dream . . . the Great Spirit tell me."

Here the Mohawks had a definite edge. There wasn't any Great Spirit telling the local allopath who was sleeping and who wasn't. So the Indians got the Miltown business. Out would come the secret pouch filled with nature's own precious medicaments—but there, now I'm doing it too. Anyway, the old Indian gave Aunt Betsy, as Mrs. Masten was known to her nieces and nephews, a tranquilizer, a secret that could be passed on only to a daughter. One thing led to another, and Aunt Betsy became the squaw's daughter, for medical purposes. The recipe passed into Aunt Betsy's hands, including the important details about a special root that had to be gathered at midnight not more than three days before or after the full moon.

"Such," says the old chronicler simply, "is the history of the discovery of Aunt Betsy's Green Ointment and its wonderful cures of burns and scalds, running sores and piles." For generations Masten heirs *gave it away*. They must have been a trashy lot. But the demand got too great or rapacity finally had its way. The precious compound, legend and all, at long last, found its way into the drug trade.

DR. KILMER'S INDIAN COUGH CURE

Consumption Oil.

This healing Syrup has a wonderful effect on those suffering with COUGHS, COLDS, CROUP, HOARSENESS, CONGESTION, INFLAMMATION, TIGHTNESS across the chest, CATARRH BRONCHIAL CATARRH, ASTHMA, BRONCHITIS, CONSUMPTION, and all Diseases of the CHEST, THROAT AND LUNGS.

PRICE 1/1½

Dose 1-2, 1 or 2 teaspoonfuls every 1-2, 1, 2, 3, or 4 hours as the case may require. Children-Less according to age.

Shake Before Taking.

Prepared Only by

DR. KILMER & CO.,
TEMPLE CHAMBERS,
TEMPLE AVE., LONDON, E. C.
MADE IN U. S. A.

Dr. Kilmer's COUGH REMEDY

This healing Syrup is intended for Coughs, Hoarseness, Colds, Tickling in the Throat, Croup, Congestion, Inflammation, Tightness across the Chest, Catarrh, Bronchial Catarrh, and Bronchitis.

Guaranteed by Dr. Kilmer & Co. under the Food and Drugs Act, June 30, 1906. No. 666. PRICE 25 CENTS.

DOSE—1-2, 1 or 2 teaspoonfuls every 1-2, 1, 2, 3, or 4 hours as the case may require. CHILDREN-Less according to age.

Shake Before Taking.

Cough Remedy is Compounded by

DR. KILMER & CO.,
Binghamton, N. Y.

Cough Remedy contains ten per cent of pure grain alcohol.

For an interesting study in semantics, compare the wording on the British label (left) with the cleaned-up version used in the United States after the passage of the Food and Drugs Act. But Dr. Kilmer was one of those un-put-downable men. Note (right) how he creates the inference that the government makes some kind of warranty of his goods.

An old sachem of the Tezucans told a visitor of how his nation lived in peace and plenty, "Until the white man came with his accursed arms . . . and his more accursed fire water." The savage doctors may have been able to exorcise some of the demons of disease with their shouts, ravings, terrifying animal masks, and rattle-shaking. But these therapeutic procedures could not cope with ordinary alcoholism, nourished upon a confidence, unfortunately misplaced, in the minimal herb content of Paine's Celery Compound. Celery addicts took the nostrum to steady their nerves. It was also remarkably effective as an antifreeze, the alcoholic content being just slightly higher than that of most whiskies.

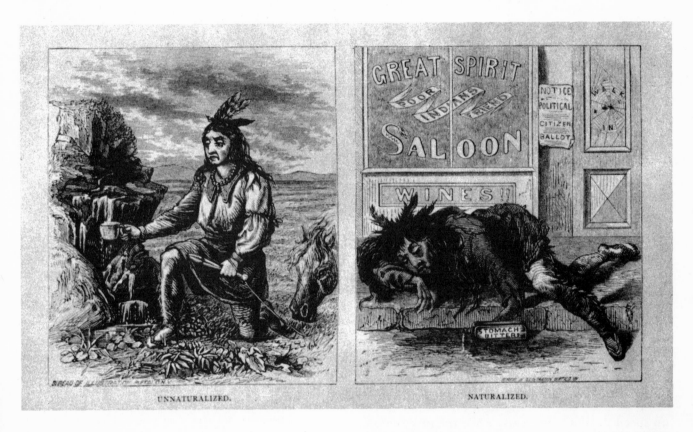

UNNATURALIZED.   NATURALIZED.

THE MOST USEFUL INDIAN SUPPLY.

When Clarence Hairy Shirt went to Omaha to have himself a time, he was likely to fortify himself with a bottle or so of Dr. Greene's Nervura as insurance against "Nervousness, Debility, General Weakness, Poor Blood, Kidney and Liver Complaints, Rheumatism, Neuralgia, Female Weakness, Malaria, Chills and Fever, Exhausted Nervous Vitality, Nervous Prostration, Sleeplessness, Despondency, Mental Depression, Hysteria, Paralysis, Numbness, Trembling, Pains in the side and back, Apoplexy, Epileptic Fits, St. Vitus Dance, Palpitation, Nervous and Sick Headache, Dyspepsia, Indigestion, Loss of Appetite, Constipation, and all Affections of the Nervous System." Clarence inevitably got into difficulties, and returned to the land of his fathers in the personal care of the conductor of the Chicago, St. Paul and Milwaukee Railroad. And to all debtors he said, "Indian agent, he pay you."

29

SHE PUT IT IN HER PAPA'S COFFEE...

The use of narcotics and patent medicines (they were sometimes the same thing) was so widespread during and after the Civil War that drug addiction became known as "the Army disease." The temperance movement, later merging into hog-tight Prohibition, picked up speed during these years, while the proprietaries prospered in supplying hooch in medicine form. In fact, the medicine factories could create the addict with one product, then cure him with another. Nostrum fed on nostrum. One item widely advertised in Southern newspapers offered to cure the "Peruna habit." It is indicative of the scale of this traffic that in the early 1900s the Sears, Roebuck & Company catalogue offered Sears' Cure for the Opium and Morphine Habit, and White Star Liquor Cure, sent in a plain, sealed package, to be administered without the knowledge or co-operation of the victim.

Papa didn't drink any booze after he had his doctored coffee. He just went to sleep. He had had his pill. Sometimes the drinker found himself taking the hair of the dog that bit him—as with Parker's True Tonic. It was "recommended for inebriates." But the Massachusetts Board of Health found that the tonic itself was 41.6 per cent alcohol.

The laboratory report of the American Medical Association showed that the Golden Treatment was composed essentially of milk sugar, starch, capsicum (pepper), and a minute amount of ipecac.

Secretly Cured the Horrid Habit

A "singing commercial" of penny-newspaper days tripped along like this:

> Where'er Consumption's victims are,
> In palaces or halls,
> Or in the rural cottages,
> With neatly white-washed walls,
> Sink not into despondency,
> There's naught for you to fear,
> By the pale and flickering taper,
> Or the brilliant chandelier;
> But drink the draught, 'twil save you,
> That bids Consumption fly,
> Take DR. SWAYNE'S WILD CHERRY,
> And do not, do not die!

Cherry pectorals were a flourishing item. They employed oil of almonds for the cherry flavor and a drug like morphine for the medical principle. Not all the blame falls on the package-medicine industry, however. Peddlers brought raw drugs to the back door. And many a regularly licensed doctor solved his diagnostic riddles with a dose of laudanum or paregoric.

As for tobacco, it too was under heavy fire from health groups and religious movements such as Seventh-Day Adventism. "A man who smokes *ought* to drink," declared Dr. John Harvey Kellogg, the health evangelist of the Battle Creek Sanitarium, with heavy sarcasm. And No-To-Bac helped build up the pressure. "Break away from this manhood-destroying habit," it pleaded.

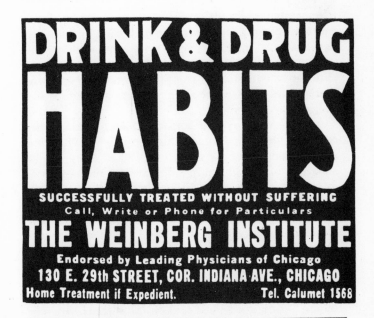

MANHOOD: LOST...

SEXUAL DECLINE.

In that field of pathology euphemistically known in patent-medicine literature as "failure at marital duties" or "loss of manly power due to indiscretions," or under the name of an invented disease called "spermatorrhoea," which meant impotence, the "professor" with the professional-looking Vandyke beard came into a rich inheritance. He played upon the guilty apprehensions of all who secretly knew that they had sinned, the lively imaginings of each one who could be persuaded that for every "weak woman" in the world there was also a weak man—himself. Nature, it appeared, had bungled the business of biological reproduction. But fortunately there was available a "make man" pill which could repair the error.

Mandrake root, with an ancient reputation for sex-stimulating qualities reaching back to Bible times, was heavily promoted by medical businessmen whose ethics were still in the formative stage. The desire for a miracle invariably brings forth miracle workers. As a correspondent observed long ago in the little health magazine devoted to Sylvester Graham's reformatory ideas, the *Graham Journal of Health and Longevity,* "Manufacturing diseases . . . is a trade better followed than any other in a growing republic." Later came ploys derived from radium and various other rays, based upon the public's voracious interest in science, and glands. Today we have our pega-palo vine and royal jelly. Credulity seems to keep up with the population explosion. It is not without significance that P. T. Barnum once wrote patent-medicine handbills. Respectable mail-order firms in the early years of this century offered gadgets to make men more virile. Lady patients, too, might become more womanly, it was said, provided they were—here comes the clever clincher—"without bad complications." The cost was modest, only $18.00, or about two weeks' pay for the average working man.

The hope of turning back the clock twinkled especially brightly for fading males during the "flaming youth" decades of the 1920s and 1930s. They sought an elixir of life in youth pills, and in various rays, pads, belts, packs, jars, mechanical developers, salts, and glandular extracts, and would gladly, as did Dr. Faustus, have made a pact with the devil to gain a few more frisky years. The history of medicine, and especially its offshoots, is also the history of man. During the national debate on the regulation of foods and drugs, the medicine advertisers attacked the 1905 bill as an invasion of personal liberty. "Where liberty reigns," exclaimed their spokesman, "there you will find proprietary medicines."

What an opportunity for a man with the conscience of a lightning-rod salesman! Take a poor but dishonest hustler or pitchman, for instance, who may have started out with "photographic cards for gentlemen—front views only," moved up in the world with a kinky-hair straightener, added a baldness cure, and then—discovered Lost Manhood, the greatest sucker bait of all time.

... AND FOUND!

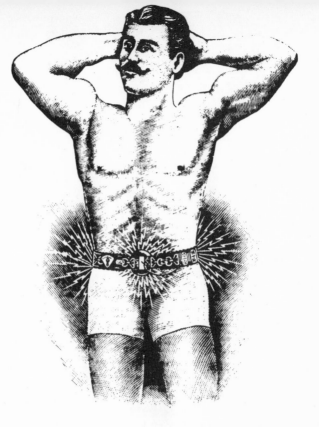

THE MORMON ELDERS' DAMIANA WAFERS.

The regenerative properties of transplanted animal glands, monkey or goat, and sly hints about male prowess under polygamous religious and social systems induced enticing reveries. But the highest hope of being eternally young which Grandpa's America ever glimpsed sparkled from the fascinating plaques of the electric belt. See next page for details.

33

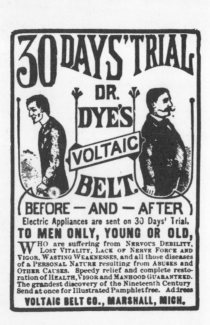

34

BE A HEALTH-BELT MAN! An electric belt was a gorgeous and impressive contraption of copper and zinc disks clamped to a belt of red flannel or to strips of red and yellow cotton flannel and connected by wires—an arrangement of metals and absorbents suggesting a wet battery. The pitch started out, "Did not time prevent, we could talk for hours upon the many wonderful things that electricity has accomplished . . ."

Worn next to the skin, the device transmitted a distinct burning sensation. This was interpreted as proof that a gentle, soothing alternating current was being applied to the wasted, exhausted organs. The kick was in the capsicum with which the belt had been soaked. All that the wearer ever got out of his belt was a dream—and a blister.

A number of products have exploited the idea that what the people of this country needed was more iron. A classic campaign in the testimonial mode was carried out by Nuxated Iron some forty-five years ago, when heavyweight champion Jess Willard fought Frank Moran. Willard spilled his secret in large-scale newspaper space. It was Nuxated Iron. For what happened later when Willard met Jack Dempsey at Toledo, Ohio, turn the page.

WHEN IT CATCHES YOU <u>THERE</u>...

When the American people took on the job of subduing a continent, cutting down the forests, grubbing out the stumps, sawing the timber, building canals and railroads and cities with the tools available, it was inevitable that the working population would be afflicted with rheumatism, contracted cords and muscles, sprains and bruises, wounds, bee stings, insect bites, frostbite, and snakebite, chilblains, earache, piles, sore throat, swollen glands, caked breasts, enlarged joints, cramps, and bronchial affections.

It took a lot of doing to build a new nation; and a lot of liniment. The forty-niners were advised by Dr. Tobias regarding his Venetian Liniment that if they were troubled with falling hair, wens, cramps, or if their horse had colic, "Californians can take no medicine with them which will be more serviceable than this liniment. Many . . . state they have paid $1.50 in San Francisco for my 25¢ bottles." There were a thousand variations open to Dr. Tobias and his colleagues for combining camphor, ammonia, chloroform, alcohol, and turpentine. But it all came out as liniment. And it all did about the same good work around the house, farm, or stable. In the South, turpentine was the great catholicon. Used externally or internally, as Professor Thomas D. Clark has observed, "It smelled loud, tasted bad and burned like the woods on fire. Southern kidneys paid a heavy price for its frequent use."

One of the spectacular successes in the liniment game was made by John A. Hamlin, a precocious youth from Cincinnati who settled in Chicago. At the tender age of twenty-two Hamlin had formulated and launched his liniment. A young man of imagination, he called the product Wizard Oil, probably because he was also a magician. Hamlin stumped the country, putting on magic performances and promising the rubes that if they would rub their hands with his oil they could become wizards too. The oil became renowned as a treatment for muscular ailments, along with massage. Hamlin personally placed his confidence in massage, an intimate reported.

Later other products were added. Wizard Oil concert companies played the small-town opera houses, carrying two wardrobe trunks, a portable organ, a supply of liniment and of *Humorous and Sentimental Songs as Sung Throughout the United States by Hamlin's Wizard Oil Free Concert Troupes*. Before the "blow-off"—the climax of the sales talk—the audience joined in singing some of the songs from the book, which were found to be interspersed with testimonials for the blood and liver pills and the cough balsam.

On special nights, Hamlin donned white tie and tails and delivered a humorous lecture cribbed from Robert J. Burdette's repertoire.

Hamlin made the grade as a businessman in the big-time patent-medicine business, firmly established his own trade-mark, gained wide distribution, blanketed the country with advertising. Wizard Oil was a snug thing. Hamlin became a theatrical magnate. His Grand Opera House on North Clark Street in Chicago's Loop, now the RKO Grand, still stands as a monument to the drama—and to liniment.

The alcohol was comforting if one could endure the ammonia and camphor oil. Out on the R.F.D. routes the people stood up to the scratching and burning and swore by Professor Low's Liniment and Worm Syrup.

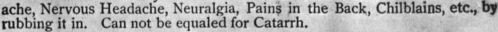

As the frontier moved West, the packaged medicines became multilingual. Hence this Wisconsin medicine, made from Oil of Angle Worm and other exotic ingredients, was advertised in both English and German.

"The Most Valuable Embrocation Ever Prepared"

The celebrated Gargling Oil was launched, circa 1839, by George W. Merchant, a pharmacist at Lockport, New York. His "Universal Family Embrocation"—i.e., moistener, rub-on—was esteemed along the Erie Canal, where it got its start, for genuine blown-in-the-bottle merit. Before Merchant's Gargling Oil was first heard of, old canallers remembered, the horses and mules along the towpaths suffered from bleeding sores, and swarms of insect pests rose in clouds from the lowlands to attack the animals. Two persons were moved to do something to ease the situation. One was a canaller's wife who made sets of cotton pants for her husband's mules. It is said that crowds gathered along the towpath to see the mules pass by in their custommade lingerie. The other activist in behalf of the animals was Merchant, the pharmacist, who cleansed the sores and applied Gargling Oil.

Word-of-mouth approval of the oil was followed

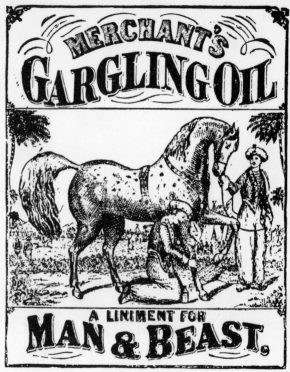

up with advertising cards, humorous and sentimental, showing horses with flowing manes. Long after George P. Rowell, pioneer advertising man and founder of *Printers' Ink,* had gone out from the Vermont log cabin where he was born into the great world, he remembered vividly his impression of the Gargling Oil trade-mark, shown above—"A sort of calico horse of Arabian pattern and vast grace and beauty." When Rosa Bonheur's *Horse Fair* enjoyed an enormous vogue in the United States, Rowell, while conceding the possibility of nostalgia on his own part, still insisted that the famous French painter had failed to match the charm of the old horse-liniment picture.

After Merchant's time, his Gargling Oil passed into the hands of John Hodge, a stunt man. One of Hodge's exploits was to send a steamboat, a one-hundred-foot replica of the *Maid of the Mist,* bedecked with banners, with the name Merchant's Gargling Oil painted in large letters on either side, through the rapids and whirlpool of Niagara Falls. On September 6, 1883, at 3:40 P.M., after a long publicity build-up, and in the sight of a hundred thousand people, Hodge had the boat towed from her moorings at the suspension bridge. The Gargling Oil version of the *Maid* survived the rocks and torrent of the rapids, crossed the whirlpool, drifted stern first to the Canadian shore, was eventually recaptured by the Americans and towed triumphantly into Lewiston at 5:20. It is doubtful if science or the arts were advanced by this venture. But it was the best show pulled off at the falls since Sam Patch made his famous leap from a shelving rock on Goat Island, more than one half the full height of the falls.

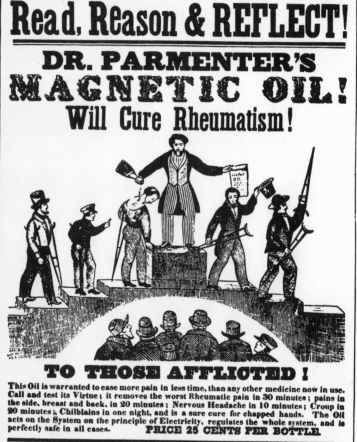

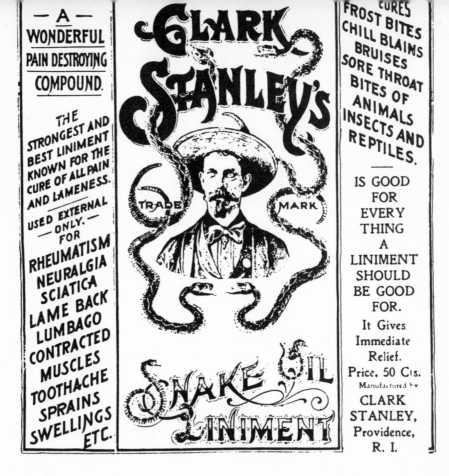

Medicine men generally have been great publicists, but notably shy of personal publicity. We know far too little of George W. Merchant, for instance, and almost nothing of Dr. Henry Wistar, the Philadelphian who first prepared Dr. Wistar's Balsam of Wild Cherry. But fortunately Clark Stanley has left an autobiographical sketch which was published, not in Who's Who in America, it is true—probably because that standard reference work was not yet in existence—but in an equally autobiographical publication which appeared in Providence, Rhode Island, in 1897. It is entitled *The Life and Adventures of the American Cowboy. True Life in the Far West. By Clark Stanley, Better Known as The Rattle Snake King.*

"I was born in Abilene, Taylor County, Texas, and at the age of fourteen I took my first trip up the trail and followed the life of a Cow-boy for eleven years. After the 'round-up' in the Spring of 1879 I started with some of my father's best friends to the Moki Pueblos at Wolpi, Arizona, to witness the snake dance which takes place once in two years; there I became acquainted with the medicine man of the Moki tribe, and as he liked the looks of my Colt's revolver and asked me to show him how it would shoot, I gave him an exhibition of my fancy shooting, which pleased him very much; he then asked me how I would like to stay there and live with him. I told him I would stay until after the snake dance. After my friends and I witnessed the snake dance, they returned to Texas, and I was so much pleased with the dance I decided to remain with them and see the dance again. I lived with the Moki tribe two years and five months, and during that time I learned their language and

dances and the secret of making their medicines. The medicine that interested me most, was their Snake Oil Medicine as they call it. It is used for rheumatism, contracted cords and all aches and pains. As I was thought a great deal of by the medicine man he gave me the secret of making the Snake Oil Medicine, which is now named Clark Stanley's Snake Oil Liniment. . . .

"After leaving the Moki Indians I went to my home in Texas and seeing some of my friends there who were troubled with rheumatism I concluded to make my first Snake Oil Liniment and I gave several Bottles away to my friends, and it proved such a success in curing them that I began to manufacture it and put it on the market. I traveled through the Western and Southwestern States and met with unbounded success. During the World's Fair in Chicago in 1893, as an advertisement I made my Snake Oil Liniment in full view of the audience, killing hundreds of snakes which were shipped to me by my two brothers.

"A druggist from Boston . . . became deeply interested, and through him I was induced to come East and I settled in . . . Beverly, Massachusetts. . . . There I started to manufacture Snake Oil Liniment for the eastern trade; finding my factory too small I decided to go to Providence, R.I., where I secured a plant much more suitable for my business."

Despite the fact that Stanley killed hundreds of rattlesnakes for the edification of the Chicago World's Fair visitors, United States chemists familiar with the snake-oil situation reached the painful conclusion that the nostrum of the Providence cowboy contained kerosene, camphor, and "turps"—but no rattlesnake oil.

IT <u>LOOKS</u> LIKE WHISKY...
IT <u>TASTES</u> LIKE WHISKY...
IT <u>FEELS</u> LIKE WHISKY...

Josh Billings, the popular cracker-box philosopher who panicked them in the 1870s and 1880s, said that if it was necessary to cheat in the "bitters" business, he hoped they'd cut down on the roots but not lower the "base." Plantation Bitters, whose base was St. Croix rum, came in a brownish-amber bottle shaped like a log cabin, with a sloping roof. The nostrum first appeared during the Civil War when there was a heavy excise tax on whisky. The patents, being medicine, were exempt. The man behind the product was Colonel P. H. Drake, whose medication was promoted by means of a mysterious combination of letters and figures: "S. T. 1860 X." This bit of occult jargon appeared on fences, barns, billboards, and rocks, on mountainsides and at Niagara Falls. It is said that Drake tried to paint his ad on Mount Ararat, the supposed landing place of Noah's Ark—see Genesis 8:4.

The explanation of "S. T. 1860 X" most com-monly given was that the cryptogram meant: "Started trade in 1860 with ten dollars' capital." But Drake insisted that it didn't mean anything. It was simply an advertising dodge to make people ask questions, like the slogan that Charles W. Post, a later practitioner of proprietary-medicine techniques, devised for his Grape Nuts—"There's a Reason." The reason was never revealed.

All the bitters boys put a generous amount of C_2H_5OH into their formulas, "to preserve the medicine." To demonstrate how much, one enterprising doctor at the Battle Creek Sanitarium hooked up a can containing a tablespoonful of Hostetter's Bitters to a gas burner and mantel. It had a "breath" that burned brightly for four full minutes. No wonder the medicine was often sold "on premises" by the drink rather than by the bottle, and that Colonel Hostetter made $18,000,000 out of his celebrated comforter.

In the spirited scene above, the Indians get the worst of it, as do competitive bitters products in the accompanying advertisement, uncharitably characterized by the Tippe-canoe people as "preparations *called* Bitters." The sachems of self-dosage were lone-wolf types. Each one not only decried the licensed doctors but talked harshly of "so-called patent medicines and cure-alls" and of the unde-sirable element which had invaded the proprietary field. Shaking his head sadly over the lies which others told, the medicine man built character by deploring vice. He was always on the side of the sufferer, and so honest he wouldn't even steal a hotel towel.

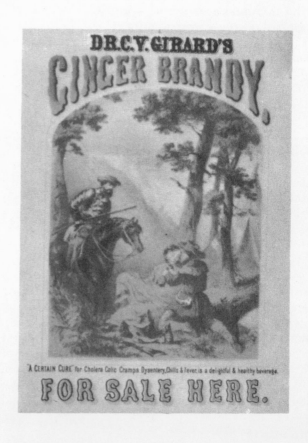

BECAUSE
IT IS WHISKY!

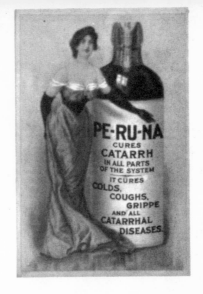

Some patent-medicine concerns sent out representatives who were known in the show-business and carnival world as "Quaker doctors." These merry gentlemen, more thespians than doctors, were got up somewhat in the style of Elbert Hubbard. They "thee'd" and "thou'd" around the tent, and called the chumps "Friend." The Quaker gimmick caught the public fancy when wigwam medicine was pretty well worked out. But notice that Dr. Flint (below) includes the Indian motif—as insurance.

A dashing personality of the period was Asa T. Soule, president of the Hop Bitters Manufacturing Company, of Rochester, New York. Soule was an engaging cuss. He sold Hop Bitters, the Invalid's Friend and Hope. Soule actually had a Quaker background, perpetuating the tradition of commercial shrewdness without the ethical standards. Soule also had a Hop Cure for coughs, a Hop Pad for distressed midriffs, as well as cures for drunkenness, drugs, and the tobacco habit. Soule was complex. He attended the Presbyterian Church, cockfights, and drove a fast pacer. He sponsored a ball team called the Hop Bitters

and announced that every player would get a dose of Hop Bitters before each game. Rochester loved Soule for the ball club and the color he injected into a humdrum environment. As a vaudeville artist caroled:

> "Hail to Asa Soule!
> Rochester's fairest jool."

Newspaper wits called Soule's team the Liverpads and Rumbleguts. The Buffalo *Courier* jeered, "The Hop Bitters have already been challenged by the Castorias, the Vegetines and the Gargling Oils." Meanwhile Hop Bitters circled the globe. Soule and a rival genius, H. H. Warner, of Warner's Safe Cure, and some others, made Rochester in 1890 the third largest center for the manufacture of ready-to-drink medicines in the United States.

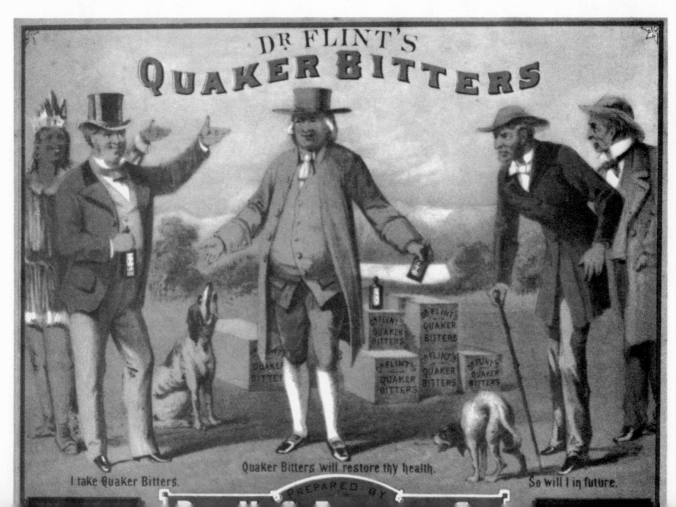

I take Quaker Bitters.   Quaker Bitters will restore thy health.   So will I in future.

THE CELEBRATED
WILD CHERRY
TONIC!

FOR THE CURE OF

ALL NERVOUS DISORDERS, DYSPEPSIA,
JAUNDICE,

BILIOUS COMPLAINTS

LOSS OF APPETITE & GENERAL DEBILITY.

PREPARED BY M. K. PAINE,
Druggist & Apothecary, - - - - WINDSOR, VT.

SOLD HERE.

It is a fascinating field of speculation for anyone with an interest in manners and morals to wonder why so much of America, especially the Deep South, the wheat states, and rural New England, voted dry on the liquor issue, but took their toddy in the form of Wild Cherry Tonic or old Dr. Worme's Gesundheit Bitters.

Look at Kansas, for example, standing there like a stone wall—for strict Prohibition. The natives of the Sunflower State voted dry for almost seventy years. And for seventy years Kansans took their spiritus frumenti regularly, under one coy disguise or another.

Odd Footnote on Lincoln Scholarship

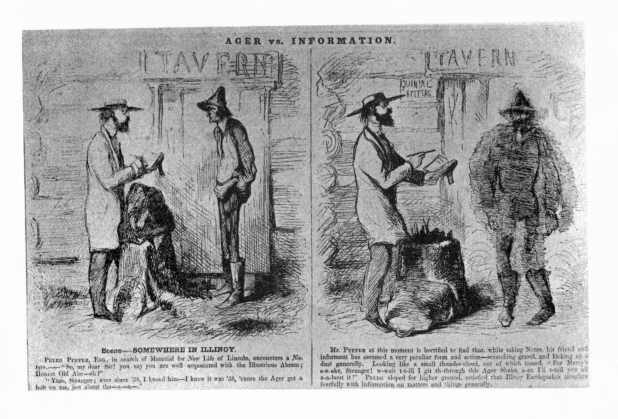

AGER vs. INFORMATION.

Scene—SOMEWHERE IN ILLINOY.

PELEG PUFFER, Esq., in search of Material for *New Life of Lincoln*, encounters a Native.——"So, my dear Sir! you say you are well acquainted with the Illustrious Abram; Honest Old Abe—eh?"

"Yaas, Stranger; ever since '38, I knoed him—I know it was '38, 'cause the Ager got a holt on me, jest about tha—a—a—".

Mr. PUFFER at this moment is horrified to find that, while taking Notes, his friend and informant has assumed a very peculiar form and action—scratching gravel, and kicking up dust generally. Looking like a small thunder-cloud, out of which issued, "For Mercy's s-a-ake, Stranger! w-wait t-t-ill I git th-through this Ager Shake, a-an I'll t-tell you all a-a-bout it!" PELEG sloped for higher ground, satisfied that Illinoy Earthquakes interfere fearfully with information on matters and things generally.

It was a capital stroke for suffering humanity when Colonel P. H. Drake visited the Virgin Islands and learned of a pure and nutritious essence extracted there from sugar cane, known as rum. This article, with the addition of some barks, revolutionized medicine, the script says. The illustration right shows the natives crushing the cane before distilling the Great Invigorator.

The sugar-cane plantations of the tropical Island of St. Croix occupy and form a large portion of that beautiful island. The purity and excellent medicinal qualities of the spirit known as St. Croix Rum, produced exclusively from the sugar-cane, are well known to all. It is the purest and most nutritious of all known stimulants, but great trouble is experienced in getting it pure and unadulterated. Adulterers and mixers of liquors (knowing its value) have done a large and profitable trade in imitating it, until it has been found almost an impossibility to get the genuine article.

Many years ago the writer of this and an invalid physician, while visiting the Island of St. Croix for their

And a Little Child Shall Lead Them

...to Aloes, Cubebs, Cascara, Senna,
and 44.3 Per Cent Alcohol

The patent-medicine trade laid the basis for modern merchandising by demonstrating that consumers could be trained to ask for merchandise by the brand name, and retail merchants, therefore, could be forced to carry it. Pe-ru-na's anti-substitution advertisement, right, is a nice period piece. Note the costumes, *circa* 1902, the array of Pe-ru-na bottles on the shelves behind the counter—a typical stock, no doubt!

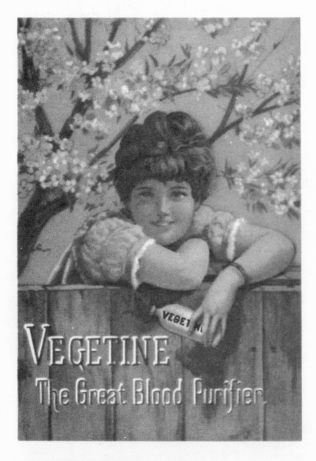

"Little drinkee?"

There has always been a fad element in popular medicines. Pills and elixirs had their run. So did bitters. There was a sarsaparilla craze; what a down-East farmer called "the great New York saxferilla speculation." It was launched by Dr. Isaac P. Townsend in the 1840s. His strengthener came in long, square black bottles—a mixture of sassafras bark, molasses, and the genial essence of cheap rye whisky. But unprincipled men, whose names appear above, dug up an old sot named Jacob Townsend, a doctor *manqué,* who sold his name to them for seven dollars a week, and Jacob Townsend's Sarsaparilla entered the fray with the outrageous claim that the original Townsend was the imitator. Moral: Both medicines made a fortune.

THE BOYS OF '61

The trend toward self-dosage in the last hundred years was a consequence of the rise in literacy, cheap postage, newspaper advertising, and the easy-money years of the 1880s. But the greatest push behind the business was the illness and disease incident to war. In the Mexican War, ten soldiers died of disease to every one killed by enemy action. In the Union armies in 1861–65 there were four hundred thousand cases of wounds or injuries against almost six million cases of illness that were consequences of dirt, malaria, typhoid, pneumonia, and dysentery, the latter known among the men as the "Tennessee quickstep." Army life meant a revolting diet, exposure to the elements, the sanitary measures of the Middle Ages—and a good share of plain human bungling. Bacteriology was unknown, but the Confederates were getting close to the new concept when they boasted in the spring of 1862 that "General Summer" would soon come to their aid—that is, malaria, diarrhea, and "camp fever."

They might have added—and the regular doctors.

Not all the patent-medicine sharpshooters were native sons. Thomas Holloway, after a fabulous success in London, introduced his pills and ointment successfully here in time to tie in with the American Civil War. The broadside shown above is of 1863. The central figure in the healing scene is, conjecturally, the "professor" himself, decked out in the long cloak of Aesculapius, the legendary Greek god of medicine. The tree and serpent are ancient symbols of the medical profession, familiar to us in the insignia of the U. S. Army Medical Corps.

A COMRADE OF GENERAL GRANT

Says: "I Do Not Believe Pe-ru-na Has a Superior for Catarrh."

BENJAMIN F. HAWKES.

Benjamin F. Hawkes, of Washington, D. C., Is One of the Three Living Comrades of General Grant In His Cadet Days at West Point.

Asceptic surgery was yet to come. But the reckless prescription of mercury in the form of calomel was still common practice. When the men went home they took back to civilian life the accumulated effects of chronic ailments, wounds, and disease and the habit of self-treatment. The patents and all manner of quacks had flourished during the war. The following advertisement is indicative of Dr. Benjamin Brandreth's contribution to the war effort:

To Soldiers, Sailors, and the Public

THE PREVAILING DIFFICULTY

A general lassitude seizes the frame, which often resembles the torpor preceding death. . . . Now whether this be in

THE NORTH OR THE SOUTH

the remedy is the same. Take at once six or eight of Brandreth's Pills

After the war patent-medicine miracles were revealed retroactively as G.A.R. comrades searched their memories under the prodding of the hungry medicine men. When two thirds of the Eighth Maine were down with typhoid, dysentery, and rheumatism at Tybee Island, Georgia, and the regimental surgeons opposed the use of Radway's Ready Relief because it was a secret remedy, a courageous noncom, one Sergeant C. P. Lord, purchased an odd lot of the Ready Relief and gave it to the ill comrades in

his company. Presto! After that not a man reported for sick call. Other procedures seem to have worked equally well. Sixty survivors of Company F, Seventeenth New York Volunteers, recalled gratefully how Dr. Brandreth had given them a supply of his pills. They were unanimous in the belief that they had escaped harm, not because of luck or poor rebel marksmanship, but because of Brandreth and his pills.

Hostetter was in the fight too. Half a wineglassful was the suggested dosage "on the eve of an engagement." Since the liquor ration had been abolished in the U.S. Army in 1832, this advice was doubtless followed with enthusiasm. On the other side, the Southerners, after downing "Our Own Southern Bitters," were able to throw off "that general lassitude . . . resulting from our long, hot summers," as Southern Bitters put it, and fought like wildcats. The proprietors, C. H. Ebbert & Company, Memphis, Tennessee, claimed to have solved a difficult problem—"The Palate and Stomach Reconciled. . . . We ask nothing in our favor but the prisoner's right, a fair trial."

From the early successes it was a short step to such abuses as the manhood tablets, bust developers, contraceptives, abortion drugs, and consumption cures which finally brought down John Law on all the packaged medicines. Some were harmless and some were vicious. But it was difficult to tell them apart. All employed the same tactics and the same gimmicks in a game that was almost as stylized as the Japanese classical drama.

A Few Choice Pages
From the Old Comrade's Five-Foot Shelf
of Patent-Medicine Literature

Primarily a Strength-Giver for Man, for Woman, or for Child,—Jayne's Tonic Vermifuge is yet the best of all WORM-EXPELLERS, those most dangerous pests of childhood. Don't be without it, either for your own use or for the child's.

THE BLUE AND GRAY.

"Oh, mother, what do they mean by blue?
    And what do they mean by gray?"
Was heard from the lips of a little child
    As she bounded in from play
The mother's eyes filled up with tears;
    She turned to her darling fair,
And soothed away from the sunny brow
    Its treasures of golden hair.

"Why, mother's eyes are blue, my sweet,
    And grandpa's hair is gray,
And the love we bear our darling child
    Grows stronger every day."
"But what did they mean?" persisted the child;
    "For I saw two cripples to-day,
And one of them said he fought for the blue:
    The other, he fought for the gray.

"Now, he of the blue had lost a leg,
    And the other had but one arm,
And both seemed worn and weary and sad,
    Yet their greeting was kind and warm,
They told of battles in days gone by,
    Till it made my young blood thrill;
The leg was lost in the Wilderness fight,
    And the arm on Malvern Hill.

"They sat on the stone by the farmyard gate
    And talked for an hour or more,
Till their eyes grew bright and their hearts
        seemed warm
    With fighting their battles o'er.
And parting at last with a friendly grasp,
    In a kindly, brotherly way,
Each calling to God to speed the time
    Uniting the blue and the gray."

Then the mother thought of other days—
    Two stalwart boys from her riven;
How they knelt at her side, and lisping, prayed
    "Our Father which art in Heaven;"
How one wore the gray and the other the blue,
    How they passed away from sight,
And had gone to the land where gray and blue
    Are merged in colors of light.

And she answered her darling with golden hair
    While her heart was sadly wrung
With the thoughts awakened in that sad hour
    By her innocent prattling tongue;
"The blue and the gray are the colors of God:
    They are seen in the sky at even,
And many a noble, gallant soul,
    Has found them passports to Heaven."

JAYNE'S FAMILY MEDICINES have no EQUALS, and families keeping them always in the house, have the BEST CHANCE of saving doctor's bills. The best Liver Pill is Jayne's Sugar-Coated Sanative. Mild and painless.

Veterans, Please Fill Out and Return This List of Questions.

Were you WOUNDED during the War?..................

If so, HOW and WHERE?..................

NOTE.—It is not alone those who were wounded who deserve our sympathy: it is that great majority WHO WERE NOT, but who contracted the seeds of disease in Southern swamps and prisons, and who have as a consequence lost their health before their time—THESE are as deserving of sympathy as their wounded comrades, and should have equal reward.

Do you attribute your present ill-health to your war experiences?..................

How has it affected you, and what is the nature of your disease?

A VETERAN PROSTRATED BY SUNSTROKE.

IT WAS ACCOMPANIED BY INSOMNIA, NERVOUS PROSTRATION AND HEART FAILURE—IT IS THE TALK OF TROY, LANSINGBURGH, AND ALL THE GRAND ARMY POSTS.

His Friends, who Knew of His Sunstroke During the War, Much Interested—The Soldier as Spry as Ever—General Interest in the Case.

[*From the Troy, N. Y., Times.*]

R. W. Edwards, of 528 Fourth Ave., Lansingburgh, N. Y., is a well-known and respected resident of that village, a prominent officer of Lyon Post, G. A. R., of Cohoes, and a past aide-de-camp on the staff of the commander-in-chief and assistant inspector for Albany County.

When the reporter called upon him he was engaged in active work about his house, something which he had not been able to do with any freedom for years. He gave the following story, which is well worth perusal:

"I was wounded and sent to the hospital at Winchester during the war. They sent me together with a batch of the wounded to Washington. Having no room in the box cars we were placed face up on the bottom of flat cars. The sun beat down upon our unprotected heads. We rode about one hundred miles in this fashion. When I reached Washington I was insensible, and was unconscious for ten days while in the hospital. An abscess gathered in my ear and broke; it has been gathering and breaking ever since. Since I took Pink Pills the matter discharged has been very small in quantity, and is steadily decreasing. The sharp, knife-like pains have almost left me entirely, and my head feels clear as a bell, where before it continually felt as though it would burst. The sunstroke which befell me on that one-hundred-mile ride brought on heart disease, nervous prostration and insomnia. I had that terrible sinking feeling at the heart, and at times would faint dead away. I became fearfully nervous, and any steady mental effort was absolutely impossible. I could not sleep at nights. Many and many a time have I got up out of bed and walked the floor with my body racked with pain, unable to find any relief. No one knows how I suffered. In addition to this, six years ago rheumatism fastened upon me, and I could not shake it off. I went to a doctor, I bought patent medicines, I tried nearly every remedy—with no good effect. As a last resort I purchased a box of Pink Pills, and it helped me to such a degree that I procured another, and still another, until up to the present time I have bought in all seven boxes. My rheumatism is gone, my heart failure, dyspepsia and constipation are about gone, and my once shattered nervous system is now nearly sound. Look at those fingers," Mr. Edwards said, "do they look as if there was any rheumatism there?" He moved his fingers rapidly and freely, and strode about the room like a young boy. "A year ago those fingers were gnarled at the joints, and so stiff that I could not hold a pen. My knees would swell up, and I could not straighten my leg out. My joints would squeak when I moved them. That is the living truth.

"THEY'RE JOHNNIES, BOYS, AS SURE AS YOU'RE BORN."

17

HER HAIR RETURNS.

Remarkable Action of a New and Wonderful Cure for Baldness.

Lady Prominent in G. A. R. Circles Regains Her Hair Although Past Fifty.

Mrs. J. S. Weed, Treasurer of Swartz Corps No. 91, W. R. C., with headquarters at New Albany, Bradford Co., Pa., owes a luxuriant growth of hair to a new and valuable remedy discovered by a

MRS. J. S. WEED.

Cincinnati Dispensary. In response to their offer to send free trials of their preparations Mrs. Weed used the remedies and although she was past fifty years of age, at a time in life when people imagine their baldness is hopeless, her hair grew out with astonishing luxuriance, much to her surprise and delight. Mrs. Weed kindly consented to permit her photographs to be sketched, one taken some time ago when she was prematurely bald and a later one taken recently showing the beautiful effects of this remarkable hair grower.

The remedy also cures itching and dandruff, sure signs of approaching baldness, and it also restores gray hair to natural color and produces thick and lustrous eyebrows and eyelashes. By sending

DALLEY'S MAGICAL PAIN EXTRACTOR

Entered according to act of Cong. in the year 1866 by H.W. Hewet, in the Clerks Office of the District Court for the Southern District of N.Y.

LITH. BY HATCH & CO. 29 WILLIAM ST. N.Y.

MOLLY PITCHER.
THE HEROINE OF MONMOUTH.
Avenging her Husband's Death.

J. WRIGHT & CO. NEW YORK & NEW ORLEANS.

The story told in the dramatic lithograph above is that of a sturdy German girl from the Palatinate who, as Molly Hays, was on the battlefield of Monmouth, New Jersey, that hot June 28, 1778. She carried water from a well to the American wounded; hence the sobriquet of "Molly Pitcher." When her husband suffered sunstroke, Molly stepped into his place and served his cannon for the rest of the engagement. The Pain Extractor ad, dealing with an historical event is, for a change, substantially true.

51

History and Melodrama
Done "in the St. Louis Mode"

Dr. M. A. Simmons, who originated his liver medicine in Iuka, Mississippi, is not to be confused with Dr. A. O. Simmons, who launched *his* liver medicine in Tennessee. The Mississippi doctor left a son who carried on the business after removing to St. Louis, under the style of C. F. Simmons Medicine Company. It was this second Simmons who used the gory scene reproduced above to advertise M. A. Simmons Liver Medicine, Chillarine, Iron Cordial—also a hair restorer, a female-weakness remedy, and a piles cure. The picture is *Custer's Last Fight*. It is not known that General Custer was a devotee of Chillarine or the liver medicine. But this kind of association between a popular personality and a popular patent medicine was frequently observable in lay medical promotion. It didn't make sense. But it was sound.

The picture is an imaginary re-creation of the disaster which befell George Armstrong Custer's detachment of the Seventh Cavalry on the sun-drenched Montana uplands on June 25, 1876, near the Little Big Horn River. The painting has had an eventful history of its own. The name of the artist, Cassily Adams, will not be found in any biographical dictionary of American painters, although he created the most popular exemplar of American saloon art in this, his only known picture. Many other artists over the past eighty-five years have been attracted to the subject, including John Mulvany, who painted a *Custer's Last Rally* and Thomas Hart Benton, who described his own *Custer's Last Stand* as being a barroom picture "in the St. Louis mode."

Cassily Adams was born July 18, 1843, in Zanesville, Ohio. Little is known of his life. But in 1885 he had a studio in St. Louis at Fifth and Olive streets, where he painted his conception of the Custer massacre. It was planned to be a traveling exhibit. But the artist was not a success as a lecturer, and the painting passed into the hands of a St. Louis saloonkeeper. Upon the death of the salooner, the Anheuser Busch Brewing Association, as creditor, got the Custer original along with the fixtures and other assets of the pouring spot. Anheuser Busch had a copy made in 1895 by Otto Becker of Milwaukee, with some interesting variations from the original. The copy was reproduced in vast quantities. Few thirst emporiums handling Budweiser Beer were without the Anheuser Busch version behind the bar before the Eighteenth Amendment closed the era.

In Adams' painting, General Custer, with flowing red tie and long ringlets of hair, is impaling an Indian with his sword. In the beer version, his saber is swung back to strike a desperate blow at an advancing Sioux or Cheyenne. In either version, the picture tells a powerful, theatrical, horrendous story. Troopers are being brained. Indian braves are scalping and stripping the bodies. The artist intended the picture to be an historical piece, a direct transcription of what happened. Its value as a document cannot be assessed fully, since the only survivor of the battle was a horse. Subsequent research has established the fact that no swords or sabers were used in the fight, that the dress of the soldiers was the ordinary fatigue uniform, that Custer had had a haircut, and that the scalping was done by women, boys, and old men.

The original painting had a fate as star-crossed as that of Custer himself. Anheuser Busch presented it to the Seventh Cavalry, Custer's old outfit, which lost it. The canvas was found in 1925 in an attic, then lost again. In 1934 it was recovered in an abandoned camp, restored by the PWA in 1938, and hung in the Officers' Club at Fort Bliss. On June 13, 1946, the painting was destroyed by fire. It is probably safe to say that in the last sixty years more people, excluding art critics, have admired *Custer's Last Fight* than any other painting dealing with American history. The basis of the popularity of the tragic scene is the disaster itself and the controversial personality of Custer. Poor history, but glorious Americana, Adams' picture made an effective advertisement for beer—and liver medicine.

THE SPICE OF LIFE...

Kissing games, "forfeits," and blowing the feather mingled with informational messages about biliousness, issued by Charles Ira Hood, who has been listed among the greatest Vermonters, dead or alive. Hood's Sarsaparilla was once esteemed by country merchants for being "as staple as sugar."

Giveaways, Games and Jokes, Cartoons, Puns, and Puzzle Cards Helped to Keep the Customers Loyal

Puzzle Card. FIND—Pelican, Turkey, Fish, Horse, Dog, Goose, Deer, Rooster, Frog, Large Dog's Head, Buffalo, Alligator and Goat.

Radio? TV?
It's All Old Stuff!

Long before the dawn of the electronic arts, the medicine grinder used entertainment to catch the attention of the customers so that he could tell them about nasal catarrh. Only the delivery system has changed. In the old days it was done with booklets and chromolithographs and almanacs. Pamphlets and cardboard novelties were offered free in the ads, handed across store counters in varying forms—puzzle cards, boffo joke cards, sentimental songsters. Puns were all the go, such as this one from a liniment flyer: "The elephant is an intelligent animal. This one always carries a bottle of Wizard Oil in his trunk. You are certainly as wise as he is."

WARNER'S LOG CABIN EXTRACT FOR INTERNAL AND EXTERNAL USE

See page 25.

HEAVEN HELP THE BOY!

He has been stuffing his little anatomy with green apples! He had a heap of fun, as they say in the West, for a little while, but when the colic began to work the cold perspiration started upon his brow, he doubled himself up in agony, and wished he had not eaten so many green apples!

He went home in great pain to his mother, who had prepared herself for such emergencies by keeping in the house *WARNER'S LOG CABIN EXTRACT for External and Internal Uses.* She gave him a few drops of the pleasant mixture, and in a short time the boy, who was such a picture of pain, became a picture of contentment and peace!

WARNER'S LOG CABIN EXTRACT is one of the most agreeable remedies for internal use, and is one of the most grateful and efficient remedies ever put upon the market for external use!

It is harmless and indispensable for household purposes, and should always be kept on hand for use in those sudden emergencies when immediate relief must be had.

H. H. Warner, a lively figure on the business scene in Rochester, New York, in the 1870s, was a safe salesman and a man with an idea. Warner was struck with the promotional possibilities of a line of *safe* remedies, with a big iron safe worked into the design of the trade-mark. Thus began the spectacular career of Warner's Safe Kidney and Liver Pills. Warner became a patron of the arts. He commissioned Henry Mosler to execute three large oil paintings in the Düsseldorf manner, at $25,000 each, one of which took the Grand Prize at the Paris Salon, and added the cachet of easel art to the Safe Kidney and Liver Pills. The outline picture shown above carried out its mission on a humbler level. It was one of many which the users of Warner's goods were invited to complete in water color and maybe win a $7.00 prize, all entries to be judged by Dr. Lewis Swift, Rochester's gifted amateur astronomer, the President of the University of Rochester, and the city's mayor. Warner's medicine empire included the United States, South America, Europe, and India. For his claim on outer space, see page 70.

55

An Open-and-Shut Matter!

A gentle but enjoyable hepatic (liverish) melancholy suffuses this advertising novelty until it is opened up (below and right), when joy and relief are unconfined. Such devices were called "fold" cards. This one, nicely lithographed by Cosack & Company, Buffalo, New York, is as interesting for its manners as for its message!

Thanks my dear, I am now relieved, We must never be without SIMMONS' HEPATIC COMPOUND in the house.

Do my dear, give me a dose of SIMMONS' HEPATIC COMPOUND, I am in pain.

EDWIN FORREST, 2.18.

PRESENTED BY

[OVER.]

JAMES' COUGH PILL CO.,

BUFFALO, N. Y.

Richard F. Outcault, the Old Master of the American "funny paper," studied in Paris, returned with a beret, a velvet painting jacket, and a disciplined talent for graphic comedy. Outcault invented "The Yellow Kid" in the 1890s (hence the term, "yellow journalism") and soared to fame between 1902 and World War I with "Buster Brown." Buster became the prototype of "bad boy" humor.

Buster and his dog, Tige, became a vogue. There were Buster Brown suits, collars, garters, sweaters, belts, cigars—and even boy babies were named after Buster. Outcault did several books on Buster and Tige, including *My Resolutions, Buster Brown,* and *Tige, His Story;* and he was co-author of a play entitled *Buster Brown.* Pond's Extract made a shrewd move when it contributed to the gaiety of the nation with a pamphlet devoted to Outcault's little hoodlum.

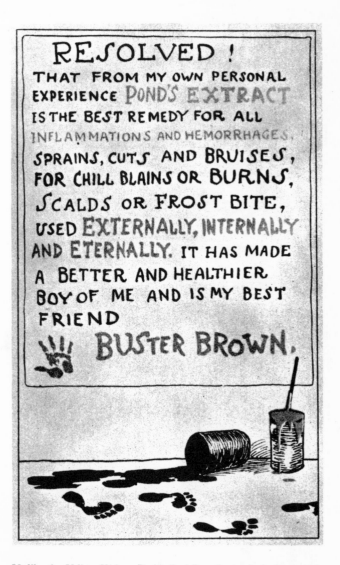

Unlike the Yellow Kid, or Peck's Bad Boy, Buster lacked true vulgarity. He was simply mischievous and naughty, a tease and a pest from an upper-middle-class home. In time the Katzenjammer Kids "made him unnecessary," says Stephen Becker, the doyen of U.S. comics historians. But in his prime Buster was a good and sufficient vehicle for spreading the good word about Pond's Extract.

All Together Now...Everybody Sing

The Bromo-Seltzer Collection

54 Popular Songs

COMPLETE AND UNABRIDGED.

FULL MUSIC SIZE WITH PIANO AND ORGAN Accompaniment

SELECTIONS.
★ ★ ★

Afterwards.
"Anna Song." from Opera of "Nanon."
Annie Laurie.
Auld Lang Syne.
Bonnie Laddie, Highland Laddie,
O Hush Thee, My Baby.
"Brother's Lullaby" as sung in "Fritz."
By the Sad Sea Waves.
Comin' Thro' the Rye.
Comrades.
Dear Little Shamrock.
Flee as a Bird.
Golden Harvester, from Opera of "La Cigale."
Hi-Tiddley-Hi-Ti.
Home, Sweet Home.
I Dreamt I Dwelt in Marble Halls.
In the Gloaming.
I've Worked Eight Hours This Day.
Larboard Watch.
Last Night (Sehnsucht.)
Last Rose of Summer.
List to Me, Mother Dear, from Opera of
Let Me Dream Again.   ["La Cigale."
Lost Chord.
Love's Old Sweet Song.
"Lullaby" from the Opera of "Erminie."
Maid of the Mill.
Mary and John.
Murphy's Head.
Nancy Lee.
Only To-Night.
Our Jack's Come Home To-Day.
Playmates.
Queen of My Heart.
Robin Adair.
Rocked in the Cradle of the Deep.
Sailing.
Sweethearts and Wives.
Take Back the Heart.
Ta-ra-ra Boom-de-ay.
The Bashful Suitor, from Opera of "La Cigale."
The Difference in the Morning.
The Garden of Sleep.
The Heart Bowed Down.
The Old Arm Chair.
The Old Sexton.
Then You'll Remember Me.
Then You Wink the Other Eye.
Thin Eyes So Blue and Tender.
'Tis Not True.
'Twixt Love and Duty.
Warrior Bold.
When the Swallows Homeward Fly.
Whistle and Wait for Katie.

BY THE

SAD SEA WAVES.

By J. BENEDICT.

What could be more amiable than the thought of the American family gathered around the cottage organ, singing "Rocked in the Cradle of the Deep," or the heady notes of the "Mustang Waltz," dedicated to the celebrated liniment of the same name? These were the first singing commercials!

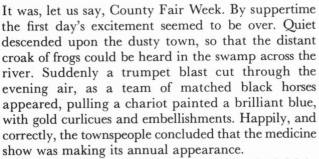

FREE SHOW TONIGHT

It was, let us say, County Fair Week. By suppertime the first day's excitement seemed to be over. Quiet descended upon the dusty town, so that the distant croak of frogs could be heard in the swamp across the river. Suddenly a trumpet blast cut through the evening air, as a team of matched black horses appeared, pulling a chariot painted a brilliant blue, with gold curlicues and embellishments. Happily, and correctly, the townspeople concluded that the medicine show was making its annual appearance.

As the gaily painted wagon approached Main Street, the "doctor" rose, dignified but smiling. Lifting his hat, his coattails flying out behind, the great humanitarian returned the tributes of the populace with grave courtesy. Small boys, many of whom had never seen even a tom show, cheered. The men who spent their lives leaning against the depot shuffled forward to the edge of the platform as the showmen paraded around the square and prepared to make their stand at the most prominent corner.

The musicians and/or Indians distributed printed flyers announcing a performance of the newest songs, brightest jokes, funniest comedies, as well as "Ventriloquial Monarchs . . . Mimics . . . Prodigies . . . Serpentine Wonders." But everybody knew what to expect. After the tunes and the variety turns, there would be a hush. The "professor" would come forward. The mood would change subtly. "Friends and neighbors," he would say, "we don't want your money. We have come to help you." If, as sometimes happened, the doctor was too drunk to stand up, he settled himself into an armchair, asking the good people's indulgence because of his age, infirmities, and hard day's work ministering to the sick.

After the clinical portion of the program was over, there would be a rifle-shooting act or a pie-eating contest. If the "doctor" was touring the Southern states, he hailed the older men present as wartime comrades in gray. On gala nights, when there was a special five-cent admission charge, any man clad in the old uniform was admitted free.

The med show was indigenous to the whole country. There were variations on the scale of the exhibition or its character—Quaker, Wild West, minstrel, and so forth. Sometimes the company were got up in buckskins as "Indian scouts." Sometimes the lecturer, clad in gorgeous robes, used Oriental bally-hoo, while he told a long, irrelevant, but absorbing tale about a precious medicinal root which had been sneaked away from the long-lived lamas of faraway Tibet.

For example, His Royal Highness Nanzetta, in private life a half-breed Mexican, wore a crimson robe and a chain and pendant which he said was the Royal Seal of Tibet. He carried the Royal Sword of Tibet too. When he went into his routine it took him a long time to get from the sword and the seal to the medicine. But the act was so convincing that His Royal Highness was once invited to sit on the platform with the V.I.P.s of Ohio when Mark Hanna delivered a speech. Nanzetta, like any television announcer in our modern version of the med show, was a "tired blood" brother in the ancient profession of Hal the Healer; of Doc B. A. Cayton and his Mo-Ton Minstrels, King Baile and his Golden Wonder Medicine, Silk Hat Harry, Jim Lighthall with his Herbs of Joy, Zip Hibler, the traveling bunionist, and all the miscellaneous saviors of humanity who ever peddled Epsom salts, corn cures, soap, songbooks, liver pads, and electric belts on the county-fair midways.

Arthur (Doc) Miller remembers medicine-show days best in terms of various high-powered aromas. There was the pungent horse smell; the odor of axle grease and sweaty harness; the fragrance of dry grass trampled by many a number-twelve boot; the rankness of unwashed human bodies and of tobacco juice. To Doc the memory of the open road seems now like a summer idyl. And there were diversions and excitements. The town gals always hung around the med shows, looking for a bit of excitement. They were usually accommodated.

Sometimes the lecturer delivered the sales pitch with a "demonstration." Thus, the painless dentist got a local chump up onto the platform—say, a farmer with an ulcerated tooth who didn't want to pay fifty cents to have it pulled if he could get the work done free. So he let the "specialist" swab his mouth out with cotton soaked in painkiller. Keeping up his chatter, waving his forceps for dramatic emphasis, the professor got a half nelson on the victim, shut off his windpipe, and gave a signal. The Indians whooped and hit their tom-toms a mighty thump. The dentist yanked. If the patient yelled, nobody heard him. The doc then gagged the farmer.

"Did I hurt you?" he asked solicitously.

"He says he didn't feel a thing," the oral surgeon reported. "And now, gentlemen, as I was saying, my King of Pain . . ."

The lecturer had to be a man of nimble wit. There were always drunks, hecklers, pranksters, and the funny, unpredictable things that could—and did —happen. Suppose the professor belched. It was axiomatic that a laugh killed the pitch. But a quick tongue could save the situation. "As you see, the herbs will expel all the gas from your stomach."

A doctor, bald as an egg, was selling a hair restorer. A voice from the audience shouted, "Why don't you use some of that yourself?"

The lecturer was too old a hand to let the yokels get a laugh at his expense. "Young man," he replied, "I heard you. You asked why I didn't use some of this wonderful hair restorer myself. *Would to God I had been able to!* But I didn't know of it until I had lost every hair on my head." His voice grew sad. "It was too late."

The heckler was one of the first to buy.

The final ingredient in the medicine show was the product. It is mentioned last because it was the least important. The constituents were common and cheap, the formula often to be found in any pharmacopoeia or home medical guide. Usually it was something that could be conveniently stirred up in a bucket behind the tent. Many med shows employed shills—that is, undercover confederates who endorsed the spiel. "Yes, sir, that's right." "Yes, yes—can't deny that." Sometimes the local hypochrondiac or eccentric made the best shill of all as he pleaded, "Say you can do something for me, Professor, say you can!" And the

SCENE IN CONNECTICUT.

30. A SKUNK OIL SALVE PEDDLER IN CONNECTICUT. ANONYMOUS, CIRCA 1875.

The medicine show, as it was known in the United States, developed partly from the jugglers and mountebanks of Europe, partly from the peddler of Yankee notions, who carried a line of cure-alls along with his calicoes and tinware. Often the hawker became a specialist, selling medicines only, could play the B-flat cornet, and gave himself the airs of an honest-to-goodness doctor. The itinerant skunk-oil merchant in the cartoon above literally blew his own horn, for one can see it, hanging at his left side. And he carried his own menagerie, consisting of one skunk.

suave doctor would assure his anonymous friend that he and the tonic would do all that science and skill could for him.

Some of the best medicine showmen were women. Princess Iola, nee Eva Billings, of Quincy, Illinois, was the daughter of a wagon-circus family. She learned trapeze work, loop walking, and contortion as a child; and later, as a show-business mother, how to pull out the drawer of a hotel bureau, prop a stick under it, and that was a bassinet. Princess Iola pitched complexion soap, which was whatever they had for sale at the local dime store, cut up into small chunks and rewrapped in foil.

Madame DuBois had a brass band, pulled teeth, and sold medicine from a great chariot. Princess Lotus Blossom was a Minnesota farm girl who later switched to a "scientific" ballyhoo under the stage name of Madame V. Pasteur. The V. was authentic. Her name was Violet. Madame never mentioned Louis Pasteur. But perhaps her cultured manner and the college cap and gown she wore suggested a good deal more to the folks out in front than she ever claimed. Madame V. Pasteur had a rejuvenation pitch which was especially written for her, she said, by a college professor. It was filled with erudite references to Ponce de Léon, Metchnikoff, and the body toxins.

The practitioners of tail-gate medicine have gone to their Valhalla now, to join Dr. George Chester and his Verona Herbs; Beeson, the Quaker; Franz C. A. Goerss, M.D. (Heidelberg, '69, he said). The alcohol tax and other burdensome federal, state, and municipal regulations, the many closed towns—these difficulties all added up to curtains for this curious and picturesque fragment of the American past.

The knights of the gasoline torch found their professional meeting place in the columns of *Billboard,* the news magazine of the amusement world. Typical item: "Dr. George M. Reed and the Mrs. are making a three-week stand at Terre Haute, Indiana, two weeks with corn treatment and one week with perfume. Had three good weeks in Peoria."

How a White Chief Made Big Medicine

Probably the most spectacular med shows of the patent-medicine decades were the Healy and Bigelow Kickapoo Indian galas. They capitalized on curiosity about the West and the vogue for Wild West shows. Pawnee Bill—Major Gordon Lillie—is said to have got into the Wild West show business through having delivered a clutch of reservation Indians to the Kickapoo interests.

It had come suddenly to John E. Healy, a second-generation Irishman born in New Haven, like an apocalyptic vision: Why not have Indian herb medicines sold by the Indians themselves in an imaginative stage setting? The Kickapoo road companies were the result, numbered from one up. They consisted of a half-dozen Indians with their squaws and papooses and a consulting doctor (the manager) who lectured on the merits of the preparations. For years there were seventy-five or a hundred of these carnival companies, known as the "Kicks" in the circus world. Each outfit carried a canvas roof, seats for about five hundred spectators, and a side wall. Tepees were erected on the "reservation." The manager's tent was placarded "Indian agent." And that wasn't entirely fiction. When Doctor Laughing Dog got into trouble over the price of a pint, it was the job of the "agent" to straighten him out.

The performers were required to do two turns, double in the afterpiece, and stick up bills during the morning. At first Healy and Bigelow visualized the medicine as simmering in a pot inside a tepee. But this was a lot of trouble. So the script was changed. Healy and Bigelow became simply representatives of the Indians who happened to be located in New Haven, Connecticut. The Plains Indians shipped their dried essences to the Connecticut palefaces. There, just to help the Indians out, the latter put the Sagwa and Indian Salve into handy packages. Why did this honor fall to the small and obscure tribe of Kickapoos? No one knows. Probably the name tickled Healy's sense of humor, which must have been highly developed.

Kickapoo was big stuff for a while—until the two partners got rich, that is. There was a full line of de-wormers, salves, and stomachics, in addition to the Sagwa. All were strongly recommended by Dr. Prairie Wolf and Little Bright Eyes.

Charley (Texas Charley) Bigelow, a farm boy from Beeville, Bee County, Texas—trader, bluffer, raconteur—thought up the rationalization of the New Haven bottling plant. The white agents were simply acting for the Indians. The little Kickapoo children gathered the precious leaves, gums, oils, and berries from God's great laboratory, the fields, prairies, and dark forests. The primitives then compounded the Sagwa, etc., and shipped it east by fast freight, where it was going to be consumed anyway.

Healy, the other genius of the Kickapoo inspiration, got his start in liver pads. The liver pad was the therapeutic novelty of the 1880s, based on the theory of absorption. Healy's pads were made of linen, with tapes for tying the pad around the body. The pad was filled, old-timers say, with sawdust, impregnated with red pepper to make it tingle—and a "drugstore" smell.

Kickapoo Voodoo!

Depending on the size and elaborateness of the show, the ballyhoo could be snakes or a variety performance. It could be Professor Balrod in phosphorescent paint, sitting behind a glare of eerie green fire, while two dusky attendants provided the beat, beat, beat of the tom-tom. Ray Black ballyhooed with a skull, a Bible, and a rope. "Snake Oil" Cooper threw out real money to draw a crowd. Or the attraction could be minstrelsy.

"Be seated," Mr. Bones would say as an opener. "How are you feeling this evening, Charley?" Finally came the Grand Old Man of Medicine—dedicated, selfless, who had toiled ceaselessly for a lifetime at the healing art, had been called in to cure kings and presidents, and had delivered a woman of the longest tapeworm ever seen in Ottumwa, Iowa.

KICKAPOO INDIAN HUNTING BUFFALO FOR TALLOW TO MAKE KICKAPOO INDIAN SALVE.

KICKAPOO
INDIAN SALVE!

Made from Buffalo Tallow, combined with Healing Herbs and Barks.

It is a perfect cure-all in Skin Diseases—for the various forms of **Tetter**, dry, scaly, moist or itchy, for **Erysipelas**, recent or chronic; **Pimples** or **Blotches** on the **Face**, **Scald Head**, **Barber's Itch**, and all annoying, unsightly eruptions of the skin; also, painful soft **Corns**, and **Burns** and **Itching Piles**.

SOLD BY ALL DRUGGISTS.   **PRICE 25 CENTS.**

☛ TRY IT !   KEEP IT IN THE HOUSE ! ☚

BONNETS ARE HIGH. A fashion journal says; "Bonnets come high this season." We do not remember when they did not, as any man who has been compelled to pay for them can testify.

In the Kickapoo shows the red men sat in a half circle in front of a panoramic backdrop. The white manager introduced them and translated their impassioned orations. "What the braves actually said, I never knew," confessed one alumnus of the rowdy Kickapoo days. But he feared the worst—"for even the poker faces of the savages sometimes were convulsed."

"From Him Who Hath, It Shall Be Taken Away"

The philosophy expressed above governed the economics and ethics of the medicine shows. The sales pitch was varied from night to night, according to the character of the tip (crowd) and the intuition of the platform performer. But in any case the aim was to capture the audience, to fix their attention, secure their interest, arouse their imagination by suggestion, and create a decision to ACT NOW. One time the professor would be gentle. Again he would be stern and uncompromising. Sooner or later he covered just about everybody's symptoms. And he said unto them:

"Time is running out; we must get on with the show. But, folks and neighbors out there, ask yourself right this moment, Do you feel good? Do you have the ability to eat hearty meals as your forefathers did? Are you constipated? Because if you are, you may already have an advanced case of *internal poisoning*. But don't expect a merrical, don't buy just one bottle and expect to arise tomorrow morning with a desire to attend the little red schoolhouse you attended forty

years ago. Don't buy that one bottle if you expect that. But as an intelligent family man and adult you can readily see the need of a complete cure. That is why we positively guarantee our six bottles for $5.00, the special family deal tonight only, and only one trip will be made through the audience. Hold it a moment, boys. Don't pass out a single bottle yet, although I see hands raised about every place out there. I also see skeptics who pooh-pooh our medicines. We have no argument with you. It's your life. But the very least you can do for your wife and those loving children of yours is to visit your lawyer early tomorrow morning and make out your will and attend to all legal affairs. You owe this small favor to your loyal family, God bless them. They have my deepest sympathy."

High and Low Pitches with Song...

GLOSSARY OF PITCHMEN'S TERMS

Pipe = a letter, say, to *Billboard,* the weekly newspaper of the amusement world

Slum = a prize of little or no value

Flukum = any liquid concoction ranging from a medicine to metal polish

Grease = salve

Chopped grass = herb medicines

Flea powder = powdered herbs

Shill = the confederate in the crowd who purchased the first bottle

Stick = same as above

Capper = the same

Tip = the crowd, the prospects

The push = the same

Turn the tip = to activate the crowd to buy

Grinder = the medical "lecturer"

Bally act = the attraction; Indians, snakes, girls or minstrels, fire-eaters, etc.

Blow-off = high-pressure selling to liquidate stock before moving on

Nut or burr = the expenses

Corn punk = medicine for corns

Corn slum = the same

Carry the banner = to sleep in the park

Lot lice = natives who arrive early and stay late without spending

Plum = a good date

Jamb = high-pressure tactics

Long con = slow, deliberate persuasion

Short con = snappy, aggressive spiel

Grifter = a concessionaire operating various games of chance

Trailer = one who trails the show, selling soda, hot dogs, popcorn and peanuts, etc., but has not paid for the privilege

Open town = one which licensed pitchmen

Closed town = one where the authorities refused to grant a license

Fuzz = a police officer; also known as a shamus

Redlighted = fired

Tripes = tripod for holding a small curb-side display case

Keister = satchel which opened out to make the case

Reader = a license to peddle

Paste = razor-strop dressing

Squawker = a complaining customer

Simp
Hick
Rube } = the rest of us
Chump
Gill

William F. (Buffalo Bill) Cody, Indian scout, actor, originator of the Wild West shows (right). Buffalo Bill once gave a rousing endorsement of the Kickapoo Indian Sagwa. Later the Kickapoo people ungratefully stole some of Cody's Indians when there was a temporary shortage. Colonel Cody's many speculative ventures included the promotion of a coffee substitute and the manufacture—with his crony, Dr. David Franklin (White Beaver) Powell—of a group of patent medicines, known as Yosemite Yarrow, Cough Cream, and Wonder Worker.

...Dance, and Ballyhoo

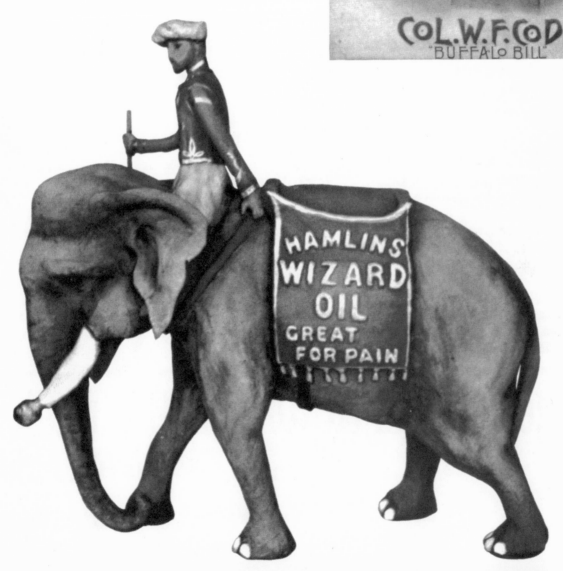

COL. W. F. CODY
"BUFFALO BILL"

The object of the game was somehow to strike the public nerve with a song, a show, a colored picture, a circular filled with testimonials. The Hamlin Wizard Oil Company laid great stress on the figure of an elephant. The one illustrated was modeled in the round, of papier-mâché, as a display for the retail druggist. Elephants were popular because of Barnum's Jumbo. And the elephant was reputed to know what was good—Wizard Oil.

67

The med show survived longest in the Deep South. When the time came to market the cotton, and a small farmer found that he was a few bales to the good, the medical thespians appeared, to free him from the burden of his dyspepsia, chills, malaria, and cash. In exchange, the physic shows provided music, excitement, humor, a most-popular-girl contest, and added a bright touch of theater to the drab life of dusty, sleepy little towns.

This joke card was used as a pass-out by a pitchman working hair restorer in Raleigh, North Carolina, shortly after World War I. In the 1930s *Billboard* was still getting "pipes" from Missouri, Kentucky, Arkansas, Texas, and North Carolina. In the 1950s the Bardex Medicine Company, traveling by truck, was under canvas, playing Georgia and the Mississippi delta country.

Mr. Asher A. Hazen, as he appeared after using Dr. Sweet's Infallible Liniment one week !

69

THE HOUSE THAT JACK ($) BUILT

In Wilkie Collins' melodramatic novel *No Name*, Captain Wragge, who had a comfortable balance at his banker's and a gig at the door, says to Magdalen, "My dear girl . . . the founders of my fortune are three in number: their names are aloes, scammony, and gamboge. In plainer words, I am now living—on a Pill!"

It was a motley crew who ransacked the old formularies. The fortunes of a cobbler, hostler, or veteran actor could take a quantum jump when he unveiled his Paradise Oil, his Buchu and Juniper Composition, his Old Jim Fields Phosphate Dill and Gin, backed up by a clever merchandising scheme. Henry T. Helmbold was a pharmacy doc who, shortly after the Civil War, became "the Buchu man," made $150,000 a year. And kept it. Dr. Joseph H. Schenck was a Trenton, New Jersey, tailor who came out with a Pulmonic Syrup for "Clergyman's Sore Throat . . . terror to the clergy and members of the bar"—and all who talk too much. Schenck stirred up a barrel of Sea Weed Tonic and made a fortune out of it, built "Schenck's Palace" of marble at the northeast corner,

Sixth and Arch streets, Philadelphia, and turned the business over to Joseph, Jr., while the senior Schenck developed his three-hundred-acre country showplace and cruised in his steam yacht—all the result of luck, pluck, molasses, and ipecac.

H. H. Warner was able to live on East Avenue in Rochester, New York, at the corner of Goodman Street, in a sumptuous mansion with towers and gothic windows. He too had a yacht, the *Siesta,* for cruising around the Great Lakes and entertaining celebrities. Warner built a private observatory for Dr. Lewis Swift, the brilliant amateur astronomer, whose discoveries had caused Rochester to feel a peculiar responsibility for new comets. Warner also established the Warner's Safe Cure prizes for the discovery of more comets. Thus he associated the prestige of scientific discovery with the nostrum which banked so heavily, and successfully, on the magic word "safe."

James Glenn Dodson made between $5,000,000 and $6,000,000 out of iron, in the form of Ironized Yeast. Dr. Ray Vaughn Pierce rang the changes on the uric-acid scare with Dr. Pierce's Anuric Tablets (fifty

70

Mrs. John Jacob Astor, it seems, had two coronets, while Mrs. Ogden Mills had three, and Mrs. William Astor, in full regalia, was worth $365,000 on the hoof. But the point was that good health is better than coronets, and

the way to good health was to use "common sense and Seven Barks." It was particularly good for nervous excitement due to the fast way of American living and urinary weakness.

"What need we of Aladdin's lamp when we can build palaces with patent pills?"

JAMES RUSSELL LOWELL

to the box, kidney-shaped, red) and other nostrums. Dr. Pierce became a prosperous capitalist with speculative ventures in the West. He owned an engine company, a hotel, and was president of a trust company in his home city of Buffalo, with a pleasure island as a retreat off the coast of Florida. Pierce served a term in Congress and could sign his chit like any member of the privileged class at the New York Yacht Club.

Many succeeded, many failed. These pages memorialize some of those who laid up treasures on earth, if not in heaven. There is room only to add a mention of Dr. J. C. Ayer, of Lowell, Massachusetts, an astute businessman and prodigious advertiser, who channeled his pill and cherry-pectoral money into paper and cotton mills and had a town (Ayer, Massachusetts) named after him. Some of the trade names he established endured for a hundred years. Perry Davis, Seth W. Fowle, who bought and boomed Wistar's Balsam of Wild Cherry, the assorted gentlemen who appear in the next chapter—all these men had in them something of Mark Twain's ebullient Colonel Beriah Sellers, who

told young Washington Hawkins in *The Gilded Age,* "I've been experimenting (to pass away the time) on a little preparation for curing sore eyes—a kind of decoction nine-tenths water and the other tenth drugs that don't cost more than a dollar a barrel . . . I wager the country will ring with the fame of Beriah Sellers's Infallible Imperial Oriental Liniment and Salvation for Sore Eyes—the Medical Wonder of the Age."

Colonel Sellers' ideas never worked. Ayer's and Pierce's did.

G. G. Green, who manufactured his Ague Conqueror in Woodbury, New Jersey, and owned hotels in California, was so proud of the visible evidence of his prosperity that he spread upon the front and back covers of his almanac pictures of his yacht under sail, his mansard-roofed mansion, spacious grounds, and "laboratory" (above). Green's palace, a real Charles Addams nightmare, was usually depicted by Green's orders in the heroic style of historical painting, draped with a velvet curtain; one is disappointed not to find Green himself in the composition, wearing a Roman toga, with a laurel wreath upon his brow.

71

View of the Glass Works of T.W. DYOTT *at Kensington on the Delaware n.º Philad.ª*

Thomas W. Dyott, a "doctor" in the sense that he had been a drug clerk in London, emigrated to Philadelphia, where he shined boots, made blacking in a cellar, saved his pennies. Dyott, full of effrontery and sizzling with enterprise, shifted to patent medicines, styling himself "grandson of the celebrated Dr. Robertson of Edinburgh," and rising "by the system of newspaper puffing," as one

contemporary observed. Dyott's Patent Itch Ointment and his Tonic Mixture were among the brash new American medications which pushed aside the old English remedies. Dyott needed so many bottles that he made his own in a manufacturing complex of fifty buildings covering three hundred acres, with busy wharves stretching along the Delaware River.

At the pinnacle of his success Dr. Dyott commissioned John Neagle to paint a portrait of himself (above). The artist was a friend of Sully and C. W. Peale, painted General Washington, Henry Clay, Gilbert Stuart, and Pat Lyon, a colorful blacksmith of Philadelphia—so why not a salve-and-tonic tycoon?

Glass collectors still prize bottles from Dyott's Kensington works, which produced fanciful and historical flasks decorated with ships, locomotives, flags, molded portraits of Franklin, Lafayette—and Dyott. The doctor went to jail for fraudulent insolvency, was later pardoned, and lived to be ninety.

What a Patent-Medicine King Really Thought About

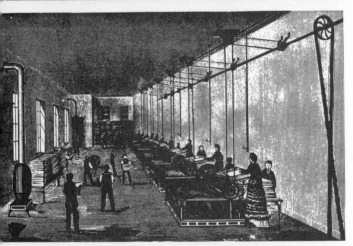

Before the federal Pure Food and Drug Act went into effect, a man interested in a secret preparation could calculate that the average drugstore in the United States sold twenty-five bottles of patent medicine every day, which added up to a national consumption of about three hundred and sixty-five million bottles per annum. It was a matter of wide satisfaction among the medicine masters that in the year 1905 the number of violent deaths attributed to the medicine industry was a mere 292. Even that small figure involved counting deaths from carbolic acid and similar poisons, which was manifestly unfair.

The point to be emphasized here about the business of snatching an ailing nation from the jaws of death is that it was indeed a business, run not by philanthropists but by men of large affairs. What they were really concerned with was the output of the "literary department"—the hitting power of their ads, and the department which audited newspaper rates and circulations and invoices and brought derelict publishers to heel. The heart of the business were the printing, folding, and binding departments, which ran all the year around, turning out circulars and little gems of pain-inducing literature by the millions of copies. Complete coverage was the advertising ideal, until every newspaper, barn, bridge, telephone pole, and store interior was pre-empted and plastered with the immortal name, so that "worthless compounds"—i.e., the competition—often engaged in "meretricious advertising," as Hostetter and Smith commented, could not be "forced upon the public."

Thus, with an occasional glance at the vats and retorts, and the bottling, corking, and labeling, a diligent, clever, and industrious promoter with a good grasp of popular psychology could make a handsome living without half trying—and die a multimillionaire. But a man had to have a philosophy about it. He had to be willing to take the cash and let the credit go. For example, Hostetter's occupation was described in a 1902 tabulation of the 3045 certified millionaires in the United States at the time as "bitters."

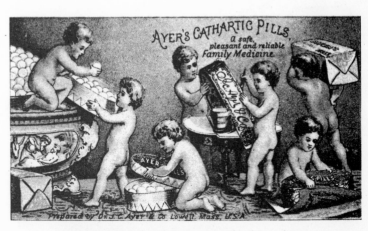

Dr. J. C. Ayer's unclothed sprites of indeterminate sex give a fanciful but not entirely misleading idea of what the patent-medicine business was all about—that is, packing, labeling, wrapping, and shipping!

SOME UNFORGETTABLE CHARACTERS

He Looked Like King Lear Tailored by Brooks Brothers

Before Southern California became national headquarters for our prophets, psychics, herbalists, raw foodists, madmen, eccentric healers, Edenists with a grape cure or a new carrot juicer, many hustlers and wierdies seem to have found Calhoun County, Michigan, a congenial locus for their depredations. Marshall, the county seat, was the home of Stuart's Dyspepsia Tablets, a rupture cure sold by mail, and Dr. Dye's Voltaic Belt, the restorative for Manly Health and Vigor. In nearby Battle Creek, T. Gorham, a gifted terrorist, was baiting the asthma sufferers. F. J. Kellogg, trading on the good name of Battle Creek and Kellogg, made his million out of the fat and the thin. The Old Indian Medicine Company manufactured a pile ointment and Wa-Hoo Bitters. Dr. William T. Bobo specialized in fits and goiter, and finally, according to a forthright observer of the Battle Creek scene, "joined his advertising agent in the seventh circle of hell." But the cream of the crop for sheer virtuosity was Dr. James M. Peebles, once a Universalist minister with a leaning toward spiritualism, vegetarianism, anti-vivisection, and pamphleteering. Peebles claimed that he had psychic gifts, sold a mail-order epilepsy cure, and contributed ten books to our national literature, including *Death Defeated, or, How to Keep Young;*

and *Soul Mates.* Peebles was tall, handsome, wore a long preacher coat, and was full of fun. Asked how he managed to reach the extraordinary age of one hundred, the white-bearded centenarian replied, "I behave myself."

But this was not strictly true.

Peebles cured fits upstairs over Minty's Cigar Store in Battle Creek in his Dr. Peebles' Institute of Health. The old gentleman had been a rolling stone. He was once consul at Trebizond, dug for shards and artifacts in the Holy Land. Caught up in reform, he had sat gravely on platforms with Gerrit Smith and Sojourner Truth. With his interest in psychic phenomena, he personally knew three thousand mediums, sensitives, and ecstatics. Possibly, then, it was in connection with a professional investigation of the psychological doctrine of affinities that the doctor was steaming up the Nile, relaxing in the company of a shapely Michigan Cleopatra, when a grand jury in the United States District Court in Detroit indicted him for the fraudulent practice of medicine.

The real charge, as so often happens, was not in the indictment. What the people actually objected to was Peebles' claim, widely advertised, that he had the power of Jesus Christ to cure illness. Recalled from his leisurely *voyage à Cythère,* the doctor appeared in court as a giant of a man with a long white beard that made him look, according to Malcolm Bingay, a Detroit *Free Press* reporter, "like King Lear tailored by Brooks Brothers. And with him in court was the most ravishingly beautiful young woman these then young eyes ever beheld."

District Attorney Gordon bellowed at Peebles, on the stand, "Do you before this jury of God-fearing men now claim, under oath, that you have the powers of our Lord and Savior Jesus Christ, to heal the sick and restore the dead to life?"

Peebles rose from the witness chair to his full height of six feet four and raised his fist above his head. He looked—the comparison is Bingay's again—"like Moses in a Cecil De Mille super-colossal."

"I do!" the doctor cried in a rich baritone voice that reverberated through the old court chambers. "I do! And may God strike me dead on this spot if I am not possessed of such power! He gave it to me. Speak, O God, and give this jury the proof! The proof!"

"The jury and I waited for divine action," said Bingay. "The air was tense. The beautiful Juno of the Nile leaned so far over in her low-cut dress that Jan [Jan Smedding, ace criminologist of the Detroit *Journal,* which, incidentally, was still accepting Dr. Peebles' advertising] got up to take a better look."

At that moment, Peebles, who had been standing dramatically with his arm over his head, waiting to be struck dead or something, let it fall in the general direction of his Cleo, spoke quietly. "Gentlemen, you see for yourselves."

Dr. Peebles was about as picturesque a healer as one is likely to come across. Although not a stomach man, he had an unusual diagnosis for stomach upsets.

"Calvinism," said the doctor, "causes biliousness."

What Swamproot Did for One Man

S. Andral Kilmer, M.D., of Binghamton, New York, discoverer of Swamproot, the Great Kidney Specific, and promoter of a line of pills, ointments, and home medicines, must often have kicked himself around the block after he saw what his gifted nephew, Willis Sharpe Kilmer, could accomplish with Swamproot and advertising. For S. Andral didn't know what to do with Dr. Kilmer's Standard Herbal Remedies after he had created them. Like many a stockholder of little faith, Dr. Kilmer sold out too soon. Kilmer disappeared medically without a trace, except that legally he did leave behind his face, his whiskers, and his M.D. degree, which were usefully employed in the trade-mark end of the successor business. But the real story of Swamproot begins with Willis Sharpe Kilmer, nephew of Doctor, son of Jonas M.

The Swamproot ads said that "Dr. Kilmer" wanted folks to write to him about their kidneys. But, alas, there was no longer any Dr. Kilmer connected with the company, as the doctor himself complained bitterly in legal proceedings which he instituted—too late—against his brother Jonas and his loving nephew. It was Jonas, a drummer for a New York woolen concern, who eliminated the shadowy figure of the old doctor from the family business. It turned out that he too didn't quite know how to reap the harvest. Then his willful, imaginative, unpredictable son came home from the Psi Upsilon house at Cornell—good-looking, dressed to the nines, full of derring-do.

Willis decided that what Swamproot needed was a massive dose of modern advertising. Willis had the Barnum touch. Under his ministrations, the denizens of the piny-woods sections of the South, who might or might not be able to recall correctly the name of the

WILLIS SHARPE KILMER

President of the United States, could identify Dr. Kilmer instantly. And so it was with the other regions of the country. Soon Swamproot was moving so fast that Willis Kilmer was able to turn his energies to dogs, horses, travel, founding a newspaper, and keeping Binghamton on the edge of its chair. Kilmer introduced golf to the Southern Tier of New York State, playing in a brilliant red cap and cloak. He was interested in horses from the days when he drove a tandem hitch from Binghamton to Montrose, New York, in a dogcart, accompanied by a groom in resplendent livery. Later Kilmer exhibited jumpers at Madison Square Garden and had the joy of winning the Kentucky Derby. He became a patron of the arts, assembling not only works by Bouguereau, Gérôme, Remington, and McClelland Barclay, but some forty-four paintings of horses, horse owners, and jockeys, all painted with the fidelity and statistical accuracy which he especially admired in easel art. Perhaps the most appropriate acquisition of the owner of the Indian Cough Cure was Charles M. Russell's study of Indian life, *The Medicine Man.*

Kilmer's first automobile was a Gasmobile, his second a red Panhard which came complete with a French chauffeur to operate it. There was, of course, an oceangoing yacht, and a favorite estate (in Virginia), both known as Remlik, which is Kilmer spelled backward. When the magnate's life and good times ended in 1940 the decedent bestowed upon his widow a sum of between $10,000,000 and $15,000,000, the choice of two out of the five estates, the stud farm, the racing stock, and the Kilmer colors.

As the preacher said in his eulogy, which was pronounced not at Paris or Nice, not at Saratoga, Pimlico, or Churchill Downs, but at the North Presbyterian Church in Binghamton to which Kilmer had allotted an organ, "He will not soon be forgotten."

And not once did the reverend mention Swamproot, or even the Prompt Parilla Pills, which many of the mourners thought was a serious omission.

S. ANDRAL KILMER, M. D.
Binghamton, N. Y.,
DISCOVERER OF
SWAMP-ROOT, The Great Kidney Specific.

"There's a Munyon Pill for Every Ill"

In the early years of the present century, one of the greats of the proprietary world was James M. Munyon. Munyon dressed in solemn black. He was portrayed in his ads with his right arm raised, the index finger pointing skyward. Munyon went in for terse sayings, such as, "If the Sign of the Cross Were to Be Destroyed, the Next Best Sign Would Be 'The Index Finger Pointing Heavenward' "; and, "No punishment is too severe for him who deceives the sick."

Munyon had wished to call his homeopathic remedies "specifics." But he couldn't do it because Dr. Humphries had the same idea; and he had it first. So Munyon relied upon the word "cure"; and it served him well enough. "Homey" Munyon, as he was called by his intimates, had been an editor, book agent, musician, song writer, teacher, lawyer, uplifter. But chiefly he was a hypnotic self-promoter. People greeted each other jokingly on the street with the index finger pointed skyward and uttered the Munyon incantation, "There is Hope!"

The federal government, however, having little sense of humor, regarded the man who said that no punishment is too severe for the deceiver of the sick as being himself a liar and humbug; and the Food and Drug Administration punished the professor repeatedly for selling treatments—for asthma, catarrh, Bright's disease, and tetter—whose chief constituent was sugar. Nevertheless, Munyon's path lay in pleasant places. For instance, he died at a luncheon table in the Royal Poinciana Hotel in West Palm Beach. The professor had a good time, with his millions and his three and a half wives. The fraction refers to the fourth marriage, which was a common-law union with a Miss J———e K————e, who made the alliance stick in court on a claim for a widow's dower right.

A Rumbling Was Heard from Maine to California

Samuel Brubaker Hartman—and who has not heard of his Peruna?—was born April 1, 1830, in Dauphin County, Pennsylvania. Hartman became a Bible salesman in rural Ohio, got himself a medical education, and started in practice with a strong anti-drug bias. Later he became a bonesetter and advertised Peruna as a side line. Hartman believed in "gentle stimulation" and Peruna had it, because of the 22 per cent of alcohol present. When the Treasury Department ruled that Peruna must have a detectable medical effect or be taxed as liquor, Hartman, then in his seventies, dumped quantities of blackthorn bark, a powerful cathartic, into the Peruna retorts. There followed a national rumbling of the bowels, especially in the more puritanical states, which abhorred the Whisky Trust. And in San Francisco there was some confusion as to whether the earthquake of 1906 was geophysical in origin or due to the new "improved" Peruna. There is a Peruna today, but a different product, recommended as a cough remedy, which meets all legal requirements. What about Hartman? Oh, yes, he was rated at about $2,250,000.

Buffalo Bill and His Medical Pal, White Beaver, agree:
"He Went Thataway"

The two veteran showmen pose for a gag shot in a Racine, Wisconsin, photograph gallery as they peer stagily at some imagined danger. Both men were publicity buccaneers in a world of make-believe; yet many of the adventures and escapades associated with their memory were real.

Dr. David Franklin Powell, known as White Beaver, got his Indian name, according to legend, by saving the life of Rocky Bear's beloved daughter. Powell was a big, handsome man, with shoulder-length hair and Western hat. He was born in Kentucky, with a spot of Seneca blood that traced back to New York State. In Omaha, the "Diamond Stickpin in the Bosom of the West," Powell picked up some knowledge of medicine, including the proprietary kind, and struck up a warm friendship with Colonel William F. Cody. Both men understood well the business of evoking the romance of the fast-fading Wild West—involving the theatrical presentation of Indian ambushes, buffalo shoots, stagecoach massacres. Cody is recalled in many a saloon with his arm around Powell, rehearsing the exploits of the old frontier and the adventures of long-vanished plainsmen. The pair were partners in a number of deals. A "reader" (advertisement disguised as editorial matter) in *The Sporting and Theatrical Journal* announced in 1884: ". . . Hon. W. F. Cody (Buffalo Bill) and Dr. D. Frank Powell (White Beaver) have 'partnerized,' and the business of manufacturing Cough Cream will now be carried on under the firm name of Cody and Powell, La Crosse, Wis."

Powell developed Yosemite Yarrow for aches, pains, and cramps; Wonder Worker, which licked cholera if taken internally and rheumatism if used externally; and the Cough Cream. He was a consistent newspaper advertiser with his cry, "No Cure—No Pay." There was a constant flow of news stories about the doctor. He became so adept at brewing political medicine that he was elected mayor of Racine for four terms. A Cough Cream advertisement provides a thumbnail autobiography: "Dr. Frank Powell, of La Crosse, Wisconsin, is a dead shot, and one of the kind of thoroughbreds nature seems to locate chiefly in the west. He is a large-featured, open-hearted and honest-eyed man, and one of the kind not met with every day."

A Muddy Brown Liquid in an Oval Green Bottle

Dr. David Jayne, of Philadelphia, claimed that he invented the patent-medicine almanac. Another of his novel efforts was to enlist ships' captains and missionaries as medicine agents, carrying Jayne's Vermifuge, a muddy brown liquid in an oval green bottle, and Jayne's Sanative Pills, to the far places of the world. Wherever there were human beings to be de-wormed or physicked, there Dr. Jayne was sure to be. Jayne erected many large and "elegant" buildings in downtown Philadelphia, took his place among the nabobs of the city, built a $300,000 mansion with doors of solid walnut, French glass, silver doorknobs, and his daughters' faces sculptured on every mantel. When Jayne died it took a will of twenty-five pages to disperse his $3,000,000 of assets. Jayne had faith in himself, his tapeworm medicine and unlimited advertising. "In some respects," observed an admirer, "he was a wonderful man."

" 'My Mamma!' exclaims the little child of our new picture," according to the printing on the back of this sentimental chromo, and the loving cry of the little one "awakens responsive sympathies, common to all mankind. Aside from all sentiment," continues the doctor, getting down to brass tacks, "we ask you to always keep a bottle of DR. D. JAYNE'S EXPECTORANT in your house."

This valuable preparation combines all the medicinal virtues of those articles, which long experience has proved to possess the most safe and efficient alterative and Deobstruent properties, for the cure of SCROFULA, KING'S EVIL, WHITE SWELLINGS, ULCERS, Scrofulous, Cancerous and Indolent TUMOURS, Mercurial and Syphilitic Affections, RHEUMATISM, GOUT, SCURVY, NEURALGIA or Tic-Douloureux, CANCER, GOITRE or Bronchocele, (Swelled Neck,) ENLARGEMENTS of the Bones, Joints, Glands or Ligaments or of the Ovaries, Liver, Spleen, Kidneys, etc. All the various Diseases of the SKIN, such as Tetter, Ringworm, Biles, Pimples, Carbuncles, etc., DYSPEPSIA and LIVER COMPLAINT, JAUNDICE and Nervous Diseases, Dropsical Swellings, Constitutional Disorders, and diseases originating from a depraved or IMPURE state of the BLOOD or other fluids of the body.
Prepared only by Dr. D. JAYNE, wholesale Druggist & Chemist, No. 8 South Third Street, Philadelphia

IT HUNG BEHIND THE KITCHEN STOVE

Once upon a time, New Year's Day was marked by a ceremony steeped in tradition—the hanging of the patent-medicine almanac on a nail behind the kitchen stove. When a man settled into his rocking chair of an evening, slackened his galluses, and felt the need for some recreational reading, like as not he took up the paperback literature provided for him by *Dr. Radway's Constitutional Almanac* or the little annual of the Burdock Blood Bitters people. Two hours later he felt enlightened but miserable. At every stroke of the clock, he realized, a human life goes out. He could feel the throb of his own ticker. Heart disease, he read, is on the increase. People are dying like flies. Who's next?

The medicine almanacs sugar-coated the pill, but the pill was always there: the ills of the body, the

The dedicated religious society which flourished in the nineteenth century, popularly called Shakers, prepared nearly two hundred different extracts and simples composed of herbs, barks, roots, and berries. The medicines were marketed by more worldly characters than the members of the association formally known as the United Society of Believers in Christ's Second Appearing. The attractive and humorous package of Seven Barks (above) contained extracts of seven tinctures—blue flag, butternut, stoneroot, golden seal, sassafras, bloodroot, and black cohosh. It was widely sold in the United States and exported to England, Germany, and France. **79**

interminable testimonials from preachers holding rural pastorates in Arkansas, mingled with jests, the aspects of the planets, the exact hour of the rising and setting of the sun, long-range weather conjectures—all were skillfully mingled with the ballyhoo for the Sanative Pills and Monarch of Pain.

The generous gentlemen who distributed absolutely free these heralds of what Norman Dodge of Goodspeed's Bookshop in Boston calls "funny medicine" did not invent the almanac; they appropriated it. Almanacs were known in Europe from the fifteenth century. They were issued here from the earliest colonial presses as calendars with astronomical data added. These little works were not advertisements. With their humorous paragraphs about mosquitoes, short historical pieces dealing with the Wyoming Massacre or the Boston Tea Party, their advice on planting and saving for the rainy day, they mirrored faithfully the interests of the rural American family. And long before the kitchen stove had been invented, *Poor Richard's Almanack* and Nathaniel Ames's hung over the fireplace, beside the clock. This was the instrument, the printed word in a powerful and intimate form, that the medical mahatmas took over for their own purposes, as pass-outs over store counters, often imprinted with the local merchant's name—as, "C. G. Douglas, Corning, New York," or whatever—with the assurance added that

> Its merits are not in the puff,
> But they are in each bottle.

Whether or not Dr. D. Jayne deserves the honor of driving out the old philomaths and printers with the dilute but free almanacs of later years, it is certain that the flood of such material did finally make it unprofitable for the old calculators to produce their ephemeris and literary miscellanies any longer. The potentates of patent medicines were not always regarded with awe.

"Whenever a man gits ded broke," Josh Billings wrote in a spoof on the medical almanac which he called *Old Probability, Perhaps Rain—Perhaps Not*, "whenever a man gits ded broke and kant think of nothing to raze a breeze with, and hiz uncle wont hav him boarding at hiz house enny more . . . he takes rubarb root, and a fu katnip blossoms, and sum tan bark, and sokes them for 14 hours in sum cheap whiskey, and

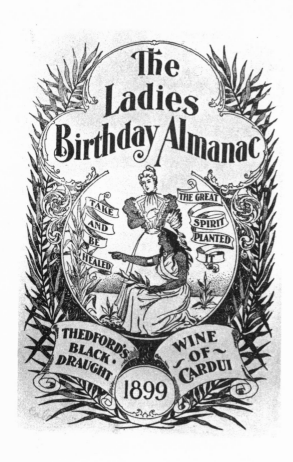

goes hedlong into the liver renovating bizzness. He plasters every fence, saw mill log, stun wall, and cow's back, from Portland, Maine to Stockton, Californy, with red, and yello hand bills, offering to heal the halt, make the blind talk, and the deaf see, and renew the inside, and outside, of all kreashun, for a dollar and twenty-five cents a bottle.... These men are ... kunning kritters, who hav found out, that mankind to be happy, must be cheated."

One way to cut costs was to leave the alcohol out, while at the same time building character with all who were attached to the cause of temperance. Vinegar bitters could be made out of a handful of dried herbs, nitric acid, and pond water. The temperance angle was worked by Dr. J. Walker, once an ill man himself, but spry at sixty-seven because of his reliance upon his own California Vinegar Bitters.

Walker charged his patent-medicine brothers with creating intemperance by putting hard liquor in their nostrums; but he, Walker, expected to live to be a hundred, and still active to the end in behalf of temperance and the Vinegar Bitters. Enough people agreed with the doctor that liquor was a serpent to make a nice business for him.

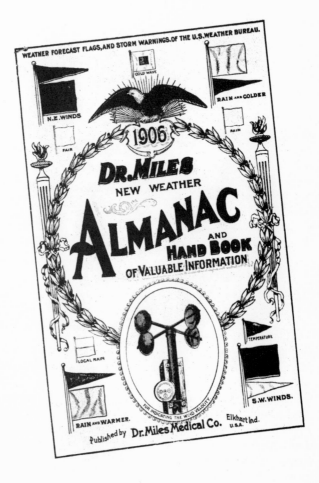

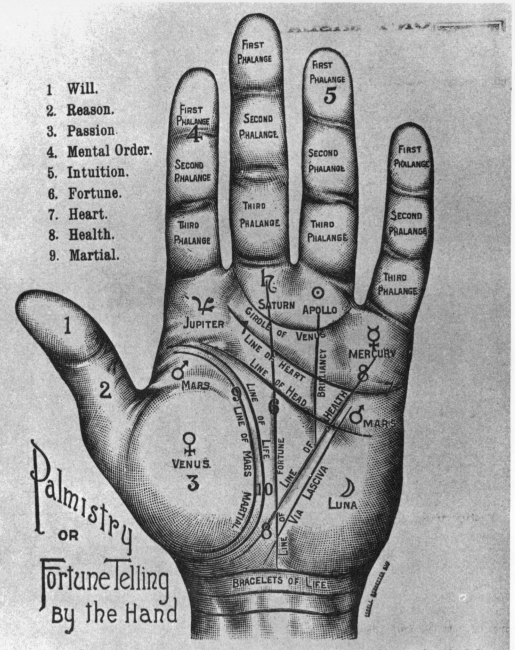

1. Will.
2. Reason.
3. Passion.
4. Mental Order.
5. Intuition.
6. Fortune.
7. Heart.
8. Health.
9. Martial.

Palmistry or Fortune Telling By the Hand

Palmistry relies upon the markings of the left hand; if in doubt, consult the right hand for corroborative indications. The thumb and fingers are each divided by the joints into three Phalanges. The intuitive faculties are represented in the first, reasoning powers in the second, and material instincts in the third phalanges.

The Fingers are named (beginning from the forefinger) Jupiter, Saturn, Apollo, and Mercury. The fleshy pads at the base of each finger are termed "Mounts," and are named after the fingers below which they occur. The "Ball" (or third phalange) of the thumb is called the Mount of Venus. The center of the palm is the plain of Mars. Below the Mount of Mercury is the Mount of Mars; extending from the last mount up to the wrist is the Mount of Luna or the Moon.

The Line of Life should, if perfect, completely encircle the Mount of Venus. A long, regular line, deep, but narrow, soft in color, denotes long, healthy life and good character. To lengthen life take WARNER'S SAFE CURE.

The Line of Mars, or Martial, should be of a clear red color. It is a "Sister" or inner line of the line of life. In soldiers it indicates success in fight; in civilians, violence of the passions.

The Line of Heart extends from the Mount of Jupiter to the Mount of Mercury. If deep, of a good color, and narrow, it indicates a strong, good heart, firm affection, and even temper.

The Line of Head runs from the base of the Mount of Jupiter to the Mount of Mars. If even, narrow and long, it indicates strong will and judgment and acute mental perception.

The Line of Fortune or Fate runs in a straight, unbroken line from the "Bracelet" to the base of the second finger. Broken lines denote troubles. Both hands should be read when studying the line of Fate.

The Line of Apollo or Brilliancy, a very lucky line to possess, rises from the plain of Mars or from the Life line towards the third finger. If straight and clear, it indicates fame in the arts, or wealth.

The Line of Health starts diagonally from the wrist to meet the line of Head close to the Mount of Mars, or at the top of the Mount of Luna. This line is unfortunately often wanting. To preserve health take WARNER'S SAFE CURE.

Via Lasciva (The Milky Way), rarely noticeable, runs from the wrist across the Mount of Luna; it indicates a cunning and faithless spirit. It is liable to be mistaken for the line of health.

The Girdle of Venus, fortunately uncommon, is as a whole indicative of a bad character.

Bracelets of Life. These encircle the wrist, and denote length of life, fortune, and happiness.

The Babylonians are responsible for a misconception that set medicine back for untold centuries. This was the unhelpful hypothesis that man's body is a little counterpart of the great world of the stars; and that the heavenly bodies exert a direct influence upon human affairs. Closely associated with the false science of the stars were other pseudo-sciences—phrenology, the significance of moles and of dreams, and the art of palmistry. Warner's Safe Cure was promoting palm reading as late as 1895, not as a parlor trick, but playing it straight.

THE ANATOMY OF MAN'S BODY.

As governed by the twelve constellation, according to ancient astrology.

The Head and Face, ARIES.

Arms. GEMINI,

Heart. LEO.

Reins. LIBRA

Thighs. SAGITARIUS

Legs. AQUARIUS.

Neck. TAURUS.

Breast. CANCER.

Bowels. VIRGO

Secrets. SCORPIO

Knees. CAPRICORN.

The Feet, PISCES.

To know where the sign is, first find the day of the month in the calendar page, and against the day in the eighth column you have the sign or place of the moon; then find the sign here, and it will give you the part of the body it is supposed to govern.

The Man of Signs, or, the Moon's Man

Indispensable to horoscopic medicine was the cut or image of a man, his viscera opened to view, surrounded by a diagram of the twelve signs of the zodiac, each connected by a line to some part of the anatomy. According to ancient astrology, each sign "governed" an organ or part of the body—Leo, for instance, the heart; Virgo, the bowels; Pisces, the feet; and so on. Before any medication was administered, it was necessary for the true believer to know whether the moon was or wasn't in the correct sign.

The reputable almanac makers became embarrassed by the moon superstition linking medicine and the movement of the planets. But the public demanded the "anatomy." As Samuel Clough sang, in his *New England Almanac* for 1703:

> The Anatomy must still be in
> Else th' Almanack's not worth a pin:
> For Countrey-men regard the Sign
> As though 'T were Oracle Divine.

The patent-medicine printers felt no such qualms. They kept astrological medicine rolling into the twentieth century. As Dr. John Bull, of Louisville, Kentucky, said frankly, his object in distributing his almanac to the "millions" was not enlightenment, but to tell them "how they may obtain and use the most effectual and valuable medicinal remedies ever produced in the known world." With increasing caution, the later prognosticators confined themselves to safe foretellings—that there would be sleet in December, that disease would be rampant among the American people during the coming year.

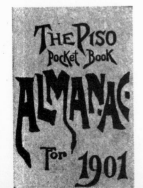

World's Smallest Almanac—Actual Size

The charm of small things was invoked by the Piso folks in this miniature "pocket book" almanac to attract favorable attention to their Cure for Consumption. After the passage of the Pure Food and Drug Act the trade name became smaller too. It went down from "Cure" to "Remedy."

The Moon's Phases...Napoleon's Escape...
Lemon Meringue...Hop Bitters for Rosy Cheeks

A Dr. C. W. Roback of Boston advised "married ladies" on the basis of astrological calculations; so also did Hop Bitters advertisements: "Ladies need Hop Bitters monthly." Notice the spiteful dig at the regular doctors—"Hop Bitters saves big doctor bills." The illustration shows the "breaking" and "scutching" of flax, once a universal winter farm chore which provided thread for the linen wheel.

HOP BITTERS ALMANAC.

2d MONTH. **FEBRUARY.** **28 DAYS.**

M	W	RELY ON HOP BITTERS.	SUN Rises.	SUN Sets.	MOON Rises.
1	Th	*Snow.*	7 11	5 17	9 39
2	Fri	Horace Greeley born, 1811.	7 10	5 18	10 51
3	Sat	*Hop Bitters.*	7 9	5 20	morn
4	Su	Cato killed, 46 B. C.	7 8	5 21	0 2
5	Mo		7 7	5 22	1 10
6	Tu	Hop Bitters, the purest and best.	7 6	5 23	2 20
7	W	*Good*	7 5	5 25	3 22
8	Th	Shrove Tuesday.	7 4	5 26	4 18
9	Fri	*sleighing.*	7 3	5 27	5 7
10	Sat	Hop Bitters for the appetite.	7 1	5 28	5 47
11	Su		7 0	5 29	6 21
12	Mo	Captain Cook killed, 1779.	6 59	5 30	6 48
13	Tu	*Mild.*	6 58	5 32	sets.
14	W	Ladies need Hop Bitters monthly.	6 56	5 33	6 59
15	Th	*Thawing.*	6 55	5 34	8 1
16	Fri	First Confederate Congress, 1872.	6 54	5 36	9 5
17	Sat		6 53	5 37	10 8
18	Su	Use Hop Bitters always.	6 51	5 38	11 16
19	Mo	*Sleet.*	6 50	5 39	morn
20	Tu	Execution of Louis XVI., 1793.	6 48	5 40	0 26
21	W		6 47	5 42	1 39
22	Th	Joana Baillie died, 1851.	6 45	5 43	2 48
23	Fri	*Clear.*	6 44	5 44	3 50
24	Sat	Napoleon escaped from Elba, 1815,	6 43	5 45	4 45
25	Su	*Cold.*	6 41	5 46	5 26
26	Mo	River Tweed dries up, 1753.	6 40	5 48	6 3
27	Tu		6 38	5 49	6 32
28	W	Hop Bitters gives rosy cheeks.	6 37	5 50	6 57

HEED THIS.—If you are in the work-shop, on the farm, at the desk, anywhere, and feel that your system needs toning or strengthening, Hop Bitters is what you need, being highly curative, tonic and strengthening.

SANKEY is accustomed to tell, as the origin of "Hold the Fort," about Sherman's message signalled to Gen. Corse, at Altoona, "Hold the Fort—I am coming." The evangelist, however, does not quote Gen. Corse's reply, which was: "I am short a cheek bone and an ear, but am able to whip all hell yet."

WHY HE COULDN'T GO TO CHURCH.—"I wouldn't be such a Christian as you are, John," said his wife as she stood in the doorway, dressed for church. "You could go with me very well, if you wanted to."

"How can I?" he half sobbed. "There's the wood to be split, and the coal to be shoveled over to the other side of the cellar; no dishes washed for dinner yet, and no Hop Bitters in the house.

"Ah, I didn't think of that," she murmured, thoughtfully, and giving her new cloak a fresh hitch aft, sailed out alone.

HOP BITTERS purifies and enriches the blood, restores health, with its rosy cheeks and pearl-like skin. Try it; prove it.

Good Cooking Recipes.

CUSTARD PIES.—Very nice custard pies are made with two eggs and two large tablespoonfuls of corn starch to a quart of milk; sweeten and spice to taste; add also salt; the corn starch should be mixed smooth with milk, and the eggs beaten up in it, then thin out with more milk; sweeten, season, pour into pans lined with paste, and grate with nutmeg over the top.

HOP BITTERS the great nourishing tonic.

CREAM FOR CAKES.—One-half pint of milk, quarter cup of sugar, half of flour, one egg. Boil the milk; beat together sugar, egg and flour; stir in a little cold milk to this, and when the other milk boils, add the mixture. When cake and cream are both cold, split the cake and put cream between. Enough for two pies.

LEMON PUDDING MERINGUE.—One quart of sweet milk, 1 pint of bread crumbs, 4 eggs, cup of white sugar, 1 lemon. Put bread in part of milk, add yolks, butter and sugar; beat together with remainder of milk. After it is baked, beat whites of eggs to a stiff froth with three tablespoonfuls of powdered sugar and juice of lemon. Cover and brown lightly.

TAKING DR. FITLER'S VEGETABLE RHEUMATIC REMEDY is the same as being prescribed for by your family physician, except that J. P. Fitler, a regular graduate, has for forty years treated exclusively Rheumatic Neuralgia and Kidney diseases, acquiring an experience enjoyed by no other physician.

Sold by all Druggists. Pamphlets, References and Medical advice, sent by mail gratis, address, DR. FITLER, 333 Chestnut St. Philadelphia, Pa.

REMEMBER, a little Hop Bitters saves big doctor bills, and *cure when all else fails.*

"A Priceless Family Record..."

Colonel G. G. Green called his almanac "a priceless family record and reference book." There was a place for jotting down births, deaths, and marriages, the date when a note came due, the wages of the new hired man. The colonel even provided a code to make diary-keeping painless. As to the weather: A = clear; B = cloudy; D = showers; W = drought; X = floods; and so on. "Make it a part of the routine home duties," Green urged, "to enter all matters of interest in these diary pages."

The Tuba Player Faced a Bleak Future, until...

The staple ingredient in all these fugitive pieces of printing, many of them now collectors' items, was the testimony of one who had consumed the medicine and affirmed that it did the business for him. Professor Ned Walton was a virtuoso of the tuba. One day his musical engagements were threatened when he contracted a heavy cold. An idea took form in his mind, "Take thou the German Syrup." As he told it, "The first 2 or 3 doses done me so much good I purchased a large bottle. It cured me."

THE "MEDICINE HABIT"

"The desire to take medicine," Sir William Osler, the great Canadian physician, once said, "is perhaps the greatest feature which distinguishes man from animals."

The People's Medical Friends well understood the loneliness of American rural life, the tedium of the farm environment, the physical and mental ills of women who had worked too hard, borne too many children. The stream of letters which came to the medicine firms written on cheap ruled tablet paper helped to keep the advertisers on the target. The medicine grinders left the practice of medicine to the physician. They practiced on the patient—his hopes and fears, the yearnings of his heart. They directed their efforts toward those people who, as Professor Thomas D. Clark has written, "sat night after night on front porches or on rickety doorsteps with nothing to do." They were perfect setups for laudanum or some variant disguised as a "nerve food powder," or a shot of busthead whisky with a "medicine" taste.

So vast was this trade that a statistical study made by a New York City doctor in the early 1900s developed the fact that more hard liquor was dispensed in medicine form than crossed the bar in the regular saloons. Some of the medicine advertisers were out and out rogues. Others had a nihilistic medical philosophy, genuinely held, that no drug would cure disease. So they administered worthless but harmless liquids and pills, relying for results on the placebo effect. Dr. S. B. Hartman, for example, stated that the patient's will to believe, strengthened by the power of the printed word, assisted by the warming influence of ardent spirits, produced good results. Claude C. Hopkins, who wrote the advertising for Dr. J. C. Shoop's Restorative, maintained that the medicine makers did more good than harm. He characterized the benefits in this way: "The good came largely through mental impressions."

The loyalty of the people who medicined themselves, and their raw courage, are as astonishing as their capacity to take the medicine. A New Yorker, W. Doane, tried all kinds of doctors for his hip trouble and ulcers, including a Westchester County root doctor; turned to Swaim's Panacea, took nine bottles; persevered with thirteen bottles of Potter's Catholicon—"But I grew no better," he said. Doane finally veered off into the Sylvester Graham diet system, and disappeared from history. A Miss Jane Demee, of Utica, New York, in five years poured down her throat fourteen bottles of Phoenix Bitters, twenty boxes of Life Pills, one hundred boxes of Brandreth's Pills, three bottles of Phelps' Arcanum, four bottles of Smith's Anti-Mercurial Syrup, five bottles of Swaim's

TAKING A PILL.

When a pill comes within the charmed circle of a person's teeth, the throat kicks. It up the shutter and closes the door. It apparently desires to go out of business. The same throat may take in chunks of unchewable beefsteak as big as hickory nuts, and other stores for interior department by the side of which a pill of the largest growth would seem an insignificant affair, but it draws the line at pills. It shuts up shop and says to you just as plain as can be: "You don't send any pills past me if I know it." This action of the human throat in the matter of pills is very curious and mystifying to the ordinary mind, and we wonder Matthew Arnold and other great thinkers have not given it more attention, and sought to make clearer for the rest of us the reason why the human throat is thus apparently so unreasonable.

You get a couple dozen of these pills, big, smooth fellows rolling about in some sort of yellow powder, or they may have a coating of sugar, and you go home and take one of them according to the rules and regulations on the box. The whole family come into the room to see the performance, of course. They have taken pills in their time, and they know there is fun in a pill performance when they are spectators only. You probably say that you are going to have any foolishness with that pill; you are just going to swallow it right down and be done with it. Then you take a pill out of the box, open your mouth, hold your head back, drop in the pill and make seven or eight desperate swallows. The pill comes up smiling, with its overcoat and a good deal of its high flavor worn off on your tongue, and you feel a little disappointed.

Some one who has had a wider experience than the others with pills will tell you to swallow of water with it. All right. You're willing to take advice in this your hour of need. You drop the pill into your mouth again and hastily drink a half a glass of water. Where is the pill now? Oh, it is snug enough down by the side of your tongue. It didn't go with the freshet. It is not traveling by water this season. "Try some grated apple," says the person with the advice on tap. All right, bring the grated apple. You are willing by this time to try anything that promises to deceive your throat to letting that pill through. The pill is covered nicely in the very center of a spoonful of grated apple, and with a weak sort of hope you throw your head back, put the contents of the spoon on your tongue, and swallow—and grated apple. The pill lingers for an instant about the palate, as if it had forgotten the word, and then comes slowly up to the teeth, leaving a good deal of its individuality all along its track.

Now bread is suggested as a disguise for the pill. This is a good idea. Why didn't one think of that before? You chew up a whole mouthful of bread, put the pill in the midst of it and make the greatest effort of your life in the way of a single swallow. But the result is not satisfactory. The bread goes right along according to schedule, but the pill is side tracked and held for further orders. By this time a good part of your taste or a bad part of the pill is worn away, and you feel that you would know the rest of it by taste at any future time in your life. Further, there are the marks of bitterness and woe and hatred of the inventor of the pill stamped plainly upon your countenance, and mayhap your feelings are such that you cannot with seemliness express them in the bosom of your sympathizing family.

Just as you have given up in despair, some one suggests that the pill is no good anyway and that something else might do. That is the best idea yet. Why wasn't it thought of sooner? Why so much ado about an insignificant pill? You are told that Tropic-Fruit Laxative, taken in a teaspoon, the same as the grated apple, that it is just the thing to stop a spell, and your rebellious throat will not compromise on anything else. You think you like the ring and are sure, on second thought, you have heard of it before. Sure enough, Simpkins, next door, keeps it in the house and comes to your relief. No quicker thought than done. The second the suspense is over, and your face lights up like that of the impecunious man who in the dead of winter and at the driest hour of a mighty dry day, finds a ten-cent bit in the pocket of a long-discarded vest. To many of us there is not much fun in taking a pill.

Panacea, three bottles of Indian Panacea, six of Conway's Boston Medicine, and a large quantity of Fowler's Solution of Arsenic, but all to no avail. Then came the dawn. "I am satisfied," she wrote, "that my life has been preserved and my health entirely restored by the blessing of God and the use of Bristol's Fluid Extract of Sarsaparilla."

"Thousands," the Kilmers pointed out, "have kidney trouble and don't know it!" They did not mention that the reverse was equally true—thousands who "knew" they had kidney trouble *didn't*. As a case-taker for one of the kidney-cure outfits once put it, "A cured patient pays no fee. Keep 'em sick!"

Humor!

The condition of the individual represented in the above picture is the result of coughing incessantly for three weeks. He has lost flesh, and is gradually losing everything else. He says:

I am fully discouraged with this and that cure,
And they say I'm a sad looking picture;
Still I'm told that for my case there is nothing so sure,
As GROBECKER'S FAMILY COUGH MIXTURE.

Sympathy!

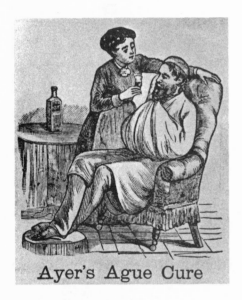

Ayer's Ague Cure

Her Bit of Theater!

OF 1,610,000 DEATHS IN THE UNITED STATES IN THE YEAR 1894, 401,000 DIED OF CONSUMPTION

THE RELATIVE MORTALITY OF THE VARIOUS DISEASES IS SHOWN BY THE SIZES OF THE BLOCKS IN THE ABOVE PYRAMID

DEATH CONTEMPLATING HIS WORK

The Andral Broca Method was a combination of worthless inhalation and worthless medicine. For his endorsers, the proprietor rounded up five ministers of the gospel who swore that the great discovery had saved a suffering Christian brother; also an ex-governor of Ohio and a judge of the Circuit Court of Cincinnati, all of whom vouched for the medic as a physician of high standing. Maybe they meant his credit standing. The judge, at least, should have known that lay testimony is not competent evidence in medical matters.

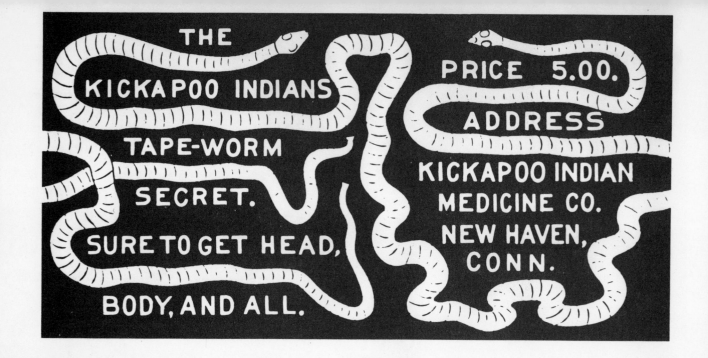

TAPEWORMS; OR,

Is the young lady agitated because she is reading a ghost story? Or could it be intimations that her privacy has been invaded by the round worm, often six feet in length and known to worm fanciers as *Ascaris lumbricoides?* She could read all about human parasites in any nineteenth-century home-doctor book, such as Dr. R. V. Pierce's fat, thousand-page *The People's Common Sense Medical Advisor.*

WHAT HAVE YOU?

If you have ever had the good fortune to meet a man carrying a pickled tapeworm, you should know that you have had an encounter with a descendant of an ancient line of specialists who work in the outlying *faubourgs* of medicine. The specialty was known affectionately in the profession as the "old tapeworm scare." He who offers to drive out evil is always on his way to a career—the more horrid the evil, the more brilliant the prospects. Tapeworms illustrate the point. The worms were highly esteemed by those who manufactured packaged medicines, because the symptoms of worms overlapped those of nearly every other disease. No line of home remedies was complete without its vermifuge, since the reign of George III, when a shop bill pictured a medicine man kneeling before the Hanoverian King on the esplanade at Weymouth as the monarch graciously accepted the gift of Ching's Patent Worm Lozenges.

Dr. J. M. Howard of Mount Olive, North Carolina, employed stick-and-carrot methods in his broadside, "Glad Tidings to the Afflicted." The doctor was the scourge of worms "from the shores of the boisterous Atlantic to the golden shores of the broad Pacific," and if you are ever in Mount Olive, drop in and see the doctor's tapeworm collection. Meanwhile, he guaranteed: "Worm in three hours, no cure, no pay."

Most of the dragon killers claimed to do their clinical work scientifically, employing big words like "anthelimintics" and "vermifuges." But Healy and Bigelow worked the other side of the street. They had a better 'ole than science, pointing out that "no disease has so frequently baffled the physician's skill [as worms]. Here steps in the uncultured son of the forest," with the Kickapoo Indian Tape-Worm Secret Remedy, sent for $5.00 with "full instructions and particulars."

Worms were essentially the result of unsanitary living conditions and the consumption of infested meats. The organisms came in five styles, from one half inch in length up to—well, Quaker Herb Extract once announced, "ANOTHER MONSTER PARASITE OVER SIXTY FEET LONG." And Dr. Alpheus Myers, of Logansport, Indiana, even took out a patent on a tapeworm trap.

WINER'S
CANADIAN
VERMIFUGE
REMEDY
WORMS.
LITH. BY HATCH & CO. 29 WILLIAM ST.

I BROKE A BLOOD VESSEL AND WAS CURED BY PULMONIC SYRUP.

You Get It...

Originality often consists of inspired borrowing. The tapeworm trick went back for its inspiration to the surgical operation to remove calculi from the bladder, performed in the sixteenth century by wandering specialists called "stone cutters." They also operated for "stone in the brain." This procedure involved making an incision in the scalp and palming a "stone" as proof of results. In modern times there came a progression, a patent-medicine adaptation of the "fake gallstone" ruse. Mayr's Wonderful Stomach Remedy was a clever humbug involving, first, a large dose of vegetable oil, followed by a saline laxative. The result was the passage of a number of soapy concretions. The customer was induced to believe they were gallstones. As was said on the package, "IT REMOVES GALL STONES AND SHOWS THEM TO YOU."

In the medical world of the patents the customer was always sure of a good show. Enormous tapeworms for exhibition purposes could be obtained for a modest consideration at any stockyard. Or an artificial worm, guaranteed to give satisfaction, could be purchased from a firm in Kansas City. If the worm turned out to be a "no show" it was explained that the medicine was so efficacious that it had dissolved the parasite. The ready-made preparations offered to grow bushy hair on bald heads, make men more manly and women more womanly, quell the symptoms or "get at the cause," fix up that asthma, dyspepsia, or bronchitis —what a spectrum! There was once even a Commanding Oil. It made the meek strong and—well, commanding.

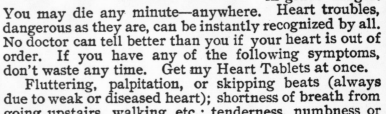

...We'll Cure It!

Whatever the compounders of nostrums lacked, it wasn't hustle and enterprise. When the organic compound phenolphthalein was accidentally discovered to possess laxative properties, it quickly appeared in the form of Purgen, panegyrized by its exploiters through a new advertising medium—toilet tissue. When Mrs. William Wilcox of Brockton, Massachusetts, had an acute attack of rheumatism she immediately received a booklet about a patent medicine. When whooping cough decimated a Sunday school in Virginia, the superintendent of the school was sampled with Raymond's Pectoral Plasters, accompanied by the ingenious insinuation that the pectoral plasters could restore attendance to normal. How could such things happen? Because the medicine man kept tabs on the health situation by means of a clipping bureau.

Again, it was the medical advertiser who pioneered the bogus news story and the attention-fixing power of unusual typographic arrangement. Purgen portrayed the Sphinx in its ads, showing the trademark daubed on the ancient monument of Egyptian civilization, because the Sphinx was a tourist attraction, or because it was the symbol of mystery, or perhaps because the Sphinx had seen everything. Colonel Drake went Purgen one better. He actually tried to paint his message of hope and empathy on the Pyramids.

Little Girl Attacked

ones are the sunshine of every home. If you have children of your own you will be interested in the story of a night attack on the life of the young daughter of C. B. George of Winchester, Ky., as told by Mr. George in the following paragraph: "Our little was attacked by croup late one night and was so hoarse she could hardly speak. We thought she would choke to death in a few minutes but a few doses of One Minute Cough Cure relieved her at once and she went to sleep. When she awoke in the morning she had no signs of hoarseness or croup. One Minute Cough Cure certainly saved the little one's life." Absolutely safe and acts at once. Every family should keep a bottle always in the house for immediate use in case someone should be suddenly

Mayer Merkel & Ottmann, Lith 21-25 Warren St N.Y.

The most remarkable thing about Rengo was its proprietor, Frank J. Kellogg, who sold both anti-fat and anti-lean preparations, and for his services to society enjoyed the use of a million dollars and the consolation of four wives. Companion product to Rengo was Protone, which put on needed flesh. Rengo took it off, not because it "turns fat into muscle," as Kellogg stated, but because it contained thyroid-gland material.

93

PERRY DAVIS' PAIN KILLER, *PARA USO INTERNO Y EXTERNO.*

DONALDSON BROTHERS, FIVE POINTS, N.Y.

PERRY DAVIS' PAIN KILLER, *PARA USO INTERNO Y EXTERNO.*

DONALDSON BROTHERS, FIVE POINTS, N.Y.

für innerlichen und äusserlichen Gebrauch.

An old minister who was well acquainted with Perry Davis and his mode of compounding his painkiller, said that it contained, in addition to various gums and the "spike," camphor and cayenne pepper—which brings to mind a story. The storekeeper at Douglas Island, Alaska, once told a visitor from New York of an Indian who came into the store one day and bought a bottle of Perry Davis'

Pain Killer. The Indian gravely removed the wrapper, uncorked the bottle, tilted his head back—and poured. The entire contents flowed down his throat in one mighty gasp. The brave then tossed the empty out the door and departed.

"Didn't he say anything?" the visitor asked.

The storekeeper replied, "He said 'Ugh.'"

94

THE GREEN MOUNTAIN
VEGETABLE
OINTMENT,

IS A POSITIVE REMEDY FOR

AGUE IN FACE, SWELLED BREASTS,

SORE NIPPLES, BRONCHITIS, SORE THROATS, QUINSY, CROUP,

Felons, Ring-worms, Burns,

SCALDS, BURNS, SHINGLES, ERYSIPELAS, SALT RHEUM,

PILES,

INFLAMMATION OF THE EYES AND BOWELS, BRUISES,

Fresh Cut Wounds, Bilious Cholic, Scrofulous and

MILK-LEG SORES, INFLAMMATORY RHEUMATISM & GOUT.

No other OINTMENT in existence of equal power and mildness for subduing inflammation and pain. Its soothing influence is realised at once, and in most instances permanent cures are effected. { See Circulars for Directions.

PRINCIPAL DEPOT, NO. 38 COURTLANDT ST., NEW YORK.

ARMSTRONG & HURD, Proprietors.

WHAT'S THE GOOD WORD? Apparently it is "Green Mountain," because there have been at various times a Green Mountain Herb Tea, a Green Mountain Salve, and a Green Mountain Oil or Magic Pain Remover. The latter claimed to cure all the ailments recited above, and frosted feet too!

Our BLAUDS IRON PILLS
ENRICH THE BLOOD.
BRING COLOR TO PALE CHEEKS.

Glide down easily.

Something for Everybody— from Eight to Eighty!

The real object of patent-medicine advertising was more subtle than the simple one of notifying the general public that a good article was available at their nearest drugstore. Unlike the modern Madison Avenue character who said in a brainstorming session, "I have an assumption, but it isn't based on anything," the panacea vendors had a very strongly held assumption: that those who were slightly indisposed could be frightened into thinking they needed what the advertiser was ready to supply. This was spelled out quite explicitly when a manufacturer reminded his druggist friends "fully seventy-five per cent of all cough and kidney remedies are bought by people who *think* they have consumption or some serious kidney ailment . . . and not by people who actually have them." It was a game of artful suggestion, of *post hoc, ergo propter hoc*— after this, therefore because of it—logic played to the limit of the printed word. And then came television!

If it don't open within 10 days, SEND FOR A BOX OF PETTIT'S EYE SALVE! ADDRESS American Eye Salve Co., FREDONIA, N. Y.

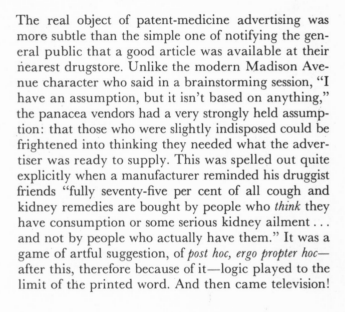

Wheels in Your Head! 10c.
Cure Anybody's Headache, as Quick as a Wink.

97

DR PIERCE'S

GOLDEN
MEDICAL
DISCOVERY

=

THE IDEAL
SPRING TONIC
AND
BLOOD
PURIFIER

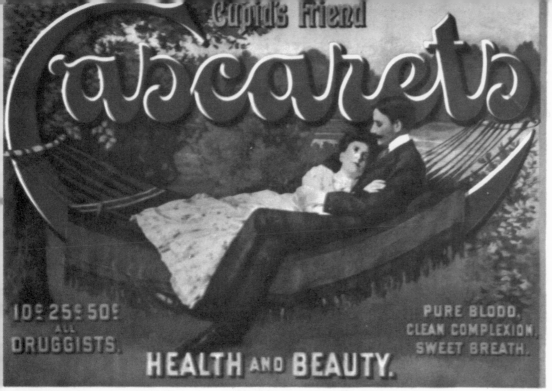

THEY WORK
WHILE YOU SLEEP

"And how is our patient today?" inquired the Old Family Doctor of Mrs. C. Moos of Fairfax, South Dakota. Only he did not put it quite that way. What he actually said was, *"Wie geht's bei Ihnen, Frau Moos?"*

And she sadly replied, *"Ganz gute, Herr Doktor. Meine Bowels haben noch nicht gemooft."*

That was, so often, the trouble.

The laxative habit was the natural consequence of the terrible beating the American stomach and gut had been required to take through a long period of history. First comes the item of food and eating habits. The national diet was heavy, starchy, greasy, and monotonous. The campfire of the frontier left as its heritage frying-pan cookery. The memory of hunger left behind it gluttony and the food-bolting of the compulsive eater. The furry tongue, the upset digestion, the costive bowel all clamored for relief.

Perhaps a greater factor was Victorian delicacy about doing "as need and nature hath us taught." Under the bed was the chamber pot. If consulted, it clinked loudly and embarrassingly. Behind every home in the United States, from the shanty across the railroad tracks to the millowner's big house on the hill, there stood a little building, the *necessarium,* like a sentry box, discreetly shielded by the grape arbor or the trailing moon vine, called rustically, the "outhouse"; euphemistically, the "closet"; forthrightly, the "privy." The rigors of a journey to this place for six to eight months of the year in the northern latitudes were alone enough to discourage peristalsis and incline the mind to the physiological theories of Horace Fletcher, the evangelist of thorough chewing, who also believed that regularity of evacuation was greatly overrated.

Patent-medicine advertising, according to Peter Fisher, editor of *Current Medical Digest,* has created "the bowel myth." Out of the weeping and wailing raised by various pills, salts, mineral oils, and "bulk" laxatives, there came a national neurosis about "irregularity." The result is, even today, according to a recent estimate in *Today's Health,* that one third of the population of the United States complains of constipation.

But . . . what a market.

One Moment, Please, while the Operator Changes the Reel

When the nickelodeon was in flower, the operator flashed "illustrated songs" on the screen while he changed reels. After the audience had sniffled damply over "The Message of the Dying Engineer" and all joined in the chorus for "Take Me Out for a Joyride," a color slide for Adler-I-Ka would appear, urging one and all to gorge themselves and trust to Dr. Adler's distinctive combination of aloes and Epsom salts to bail them out of any gastric sequelae.

PLUTO WATER
America's Physic

Uncle Sam Wants You

Whiskers in all varieties and styles have always adorned proprietary-medicine labels since the invention of wood engraving, possibly because the balmy days of patent medicines coincided with the beard period—but more probably because the beard was an important status symbol. The picture of a man with a fashionable beard on a packaged medicine said, instantaneously, "learned physician." Dr. Kilmer had his mutton chops. Doctor Peebles was magnificently decorated. Gaylord Wilshire and John R. (Goat Gland) Brinkley fancied the Vandyke. But Pluto Water went a step farther and borrowed the most famous beard in America—Uncle Sam's. Uncle Sam, the man in the drawings and cartoons who wants capital and labor to work together; the man who in wartime calls upon us to enlist, to save food, to buy government bonds—Uncle Sam plunked for Pluto Water! The striking illustration on the drugstore display reproduced above also carries a skillful suggestion that the U. S. government guarantees the product.

JUMBO FEEDS BABY CASTORIA

From peasant nurse to high born lady,
All mothers know what's good for baby.
CASTORIA.

While Jumbo, too, though not a lady,
Follows suit and feeds the great baby
CASTORIA.

In his most fanciful dreamings it is doubtful whether P. T. Barnum could have conceived his hold on future generations. Barnum is remembered for many reasons, not the least of which is his huge African elephant, Jumbo, regarded in his time as the greatest beast in the world.

The cablegram quoted above played a part in the international uproar that occurred when Barnum purchased the pachyderm from the Royal Zoological Society in London and moved him to the United States. For three and a half years Jumbo toured America in Barnum's circus. He was ridden by an estimated million children, pampered with peanuts, sustained with the finest elephant hay plus a toddy of one quart of whisky per diem. When Jumbo was killed by a Grand Trunk freight engine at St. Thomas, Ontario, Barnum was quick to announce that Jumbo

had died a hero's death, sacrificing his life in a noble effort to save the baby elephant, Tom Thumb. The sense of loss was worldwide.

Jumbo was the most influential of all advertising animals. The thread companies used whimsical illustrations of Jumbo pulling some massive object with their thread to suggest the strength of the filaments. Jumbo was shown giving the baby elephant Castoria in an imaginary tropical setting. Because the elephant was known never to forget a favor, it was surmised that Jumbo himself remembered being raised on Castoria back in the jungles of Africa.

It is with a heavy heart that one contemplates an America without Carter's Little Liver Pills. But we must face the facts. After sixteen years of litigation, 149 hearings, and 11,000 pages of testimony, the United States Supreme Court has upheld the Federal Trade Commission in objecting to the word "Liver." But the country is not going to be left stranded. The popular remedy is still available as Carter's Little Pills, still willing to help us all strike off the chains of the laxative habit.

When Horse Salts Saw Their Finest Hour

Many devotees of self-treatment have been frightened by a fanciful bowel folklore into believing that "irregularity" leads to biliousness, diabetes, dyspepsia, nervous and other serious disturbances. Three women, for example, reputedly mental cases, were reported to have drunk the healing waters from a remarkable spring containing natural laxative chemicals. The minerals present in the water, Glauber's and Epsom salts—long known as a reliable horse medicine—were credited with restoring the ladies' sanity. The American Indian had fixed periods for a ritual of catharsis, such as the green-corn feast. The white fathers scoured their intestinal tracts with patent medicines throughout the four seasons to head off a long list of afflictions. They overlooked one: *the laxative habit.*

"Second Only to Christianity . . ."

WHY YES! ITS EQUAL TO AN HOUR'S WALK
OR A DRAUGHT OF MORNING DEW

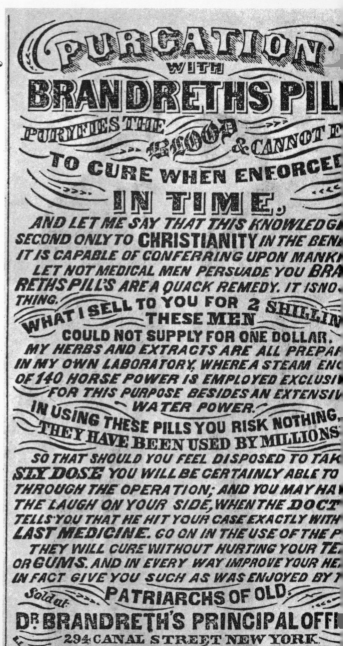

PURGATION WITH BRANDRETHS PILLS PURIFIES THE BLOOD & CANNOT FAIL TO CURE WHEN ENFORCED IN TIME, AND LET ME SAY THAT THIS KNOWLEDGE SECOND ONLY TO CHRISTIANITY IN THE BENEFIT IT IS CAPABLE OF CONFERRING UPON MANKIND LET NOT MEDICAL MEN PERSUADE YOU BRANDRETHS PILL'S ARE A QUACK REMEDY. IT ISNO SUCH THING. WHAT I SELL TO YOU FOR 2 SHILLINGS THESE MEN COULD NOT SUPPLY FOR ONE DOLLAR. MY HERBS AND EXTRACTS ARE ALL PREPARED IN MY OWN LABORATORY, WHERE A STEAM ENGINE OF 140 HORSE POWER IS EMPLOYED EXCLUSIVELY FOR THIS PURPOSE BESIDES AN EXTENSIVE WATER POWER. IN USING THESE PILLS YOU RISK NOTHING, THEY HAVE BEEN USED BY MILLIONS, SO THAT SHOULD YOU FEEL DISPOSED TO TAKE SIX DOSE YOU WILL BE CERTAINLY ABLE TO GET THROUGH THE OPERATION; AND YOU MAY HAVE THE LAUGH ON YOUR SIDE, WHEN THE DOCTOR TELLS YOU THAT HE HIT YOUR CASE EXACTLY WITH HIS LAST MEDICINE. GO ON IN THE USE OF THE PILLS THEY WILL CURE WITHOUT HURTING YOUR TEETH OR GUMS. AND IN EVERY WAY IMPROVE YOUR HEALTH IN FACT GIVE YOU SUCH AS WAS ENJOYED BY THE PATRIARCHS OF OLD Sold at DR BRANDRETH'S PRINCIPAL OFFICE 294 CANAL STREET NEW YORK AND BY ALL DRUGGISTS

"GAS PIPE" THERAPY

Pads...coils...wires, and nickel-plated pipes...ray machines...<u>electricity</u> is what this country needs for health

There is a powerful element of suggestion connected with medical treatments emanating from a mysterious mechanical or electrical device. Rays, vibrations, oscillators, Rube Goldbergian apparatus have a compelling attraction for the forward-looking, gadget-minded patient. The type has always existed. Look back for a moment at the bosomy babe (right). She has obviously put a hex on the hovering figure of Death with her malaria pad, while the gentleman across the way, unpadded, is succumbing to the miasmic vapors of a singularly unattractive watercourse.

103

You Pays Your Money
and You Takes Your Choice

J. P. Dargitz, who used to "pound brass" as telegraph agent at various little side track offices on the Chicago, Burlington and Quincy Railroad got all fired up about magnetism as a curative agent. Dargitz bought his wife a magnetic vest. He put a little magnetic cap on his baby daughter, and her bowels moved in fifteen minutes. One day he was riding the accommodation known locally as "Old Jerk" from Quincy, Illinois, down to Louisiana, Missouri, when the conductor mentioned that he had a splitting headache. Dargitz whipped a magnetic cap out of his grip and asked the conductor, William Malloy, to put it on. And so one thing led to another. Before he quite knew it, Dargitz was outfitting the railroad boys with the esoteric products of the Chicago Magnetic Shield Company: insoles, vests, caps and belts, leggings, anklets, wristlets, shoulder, sciatic, and hernial shields. "If you want to know what they are good for," Dargitz admonished his former comrades, "read the testimonials."

Another man had a finger ring that cured rheumatism, and he printed letters from *his* believers too. The Cartilage Company manufactured a contraption of straps, cords, pulleys, and cast iron that would straighten bowlegs, broaden the shoulders, and add from two to five inches to the height. The Sanden Electric Company had a little vitalizer that was designed especially for men lacking in manly strength. There was also the Depolaray, the Oscilloclast, the Oscilloton, Depolaton, Electropad, and the Electropoise, invention of Dr. Hercules Sanche. It was a nickel-plated brass tube filled with plaster of Paris, with a metallic cord to go around the ankle. The pipe, immersed in water, was prescribed for hardening of the arteries and varicose veins. Just as the Edenists, who looked back to a Golden Age, could appeal effectively to those who longed for the Good Old Days, the mechanical quacks gulled the forward-lookers with the jargon of pseudo-science.

With no plant investment and slight labor cost, the exploiters of drugless quackery reaped enormous profits. Still, their pipes and wires did cost something. So an improvement was introduced by Alois P. Swoboda, who asked intimate questions, such as, "Is it necessary to drive yourself into performing your duties?" He offered a system of exercise sold by mail, called Conscious Evolution, which didn't mean anything, or cost anything, being simply typewritten instructions.

ELECTRICITY – <u>It's</u> Wonderful

For his suckers, who were saluted as "Swobodians," the body-culture-and-rhythm man would do almost anything, cure a long "laundry list" of diseases or let them in on a hot oil stock. Swoboda explained about the oil: "I personally do not care for my own sake, but merely to aid Swobodians." Possibly true; oil prospecting is chancy. Conscious Evolution was a sure thing.

Mechanical devices exploiting medical fashions were not brought under the authority of the federal Food, Drug, and Cosmetic Act until 1938. Since then the Food wond Drug Administration has had a busy time catching up.

ELECTRICITY AS EXERCISE

RIGHT OFF THE COB

The advances in the graphic arts which made it possible for Currier & Ives to create and distribute the lithographs which Nathaniel Currier called "Colored Engravings for the people" prepared the way for the great "card craze" which swept the United States from the '70s to the '90s. Reproduced in bright colors, the chromolithographed trade or advertising cards advanced upon a drab steel-engraving world, and the folks down on the farm, starved for recreation, saw with mounting excitement Lily Langtry seated beneath a display for Brown's Iron Bitters; Mrs. Grover Cleveland, the White House bride; Jumbo, "The Greatest Mastodon on Earth"; and the sturdy, blooming grandchildren of Mrs. Lydia E. Pinkham.

"Paste them in your album," Mrs. Pinkham advised, as she sowed the bits of cardboard broadcast across the land. "Yours for health."

The lively and often well-printed cards were turned out in astronomical quantities, to be inserted with packaged goods, mailed out, or handed over the counters of retail stores to favored customers. In subject, they covered a wide range—clothing, groceries, soaps, seeds, tobacco, stoves, sewing machines, thread. And of course medicines. Many of the cards, ingenious in form, were known as "fold" or "mechanical" cards. Being capable of movement, they were wonderfully well adapted to milk the immortal before-and-after theme. First the consumer would be pictured in the depth of despair (without product); then overjoyed (with product), as the card was manipulated.

Albums containing hundreds of these little cards occupied a place of honor on the onyx-topped table in the parlor, along with the Bible and the latest subscription book unloaded upon the innocent by some merciless canvasser. The cards fell into two general categories. Some were stock cards, floral, scenic, comic, to be imprinted later with a retail merchant's name. The illustrations on these cards had no relationship to any particular product. Other cards associated the picture directly with the product. These were true advertising cards. They helped to introduce consumer goods and to establish new standards of style, comfort, and leisure. They were homely, in a good, honest sense of the word, and tell us much about the clothes people wore, the food they ate, the pleasures they enjoyed, the songs they sang, the jokes they laughed at. Most Americans didn't know much about art, but they knew what they liked. They liked pictures of pretty babies, pictures that told a story, dainty little girls, and dogs and kittens in genre situations. Dr. Schenck, Colonel Green, Hodge, of Merchant's

Who, seeing this engaging domestic scene of mother and child at play, would suppose that the chief of the Division of Drugs of the U.S. Department of Agriculture could have been mean enough to list the syrup as a medicine containing the habit-forming narcotic, morphine sulphate? Mrs. Winslow was in real life two brothers named Curtis, who lived in great elegance on Second Place, in Brooklyn, New York.

"PAPA HAS A HEADACHE."

Many medicinal "album" cards were issued in sets or series. The game was, of course, to complete the set. The back of the card interpreted the meaning or "story" told by the picture, although it was usually evident enough. Then the text got down to business: "We have no wish, however, to disguise the main purpose of its issuance, which is to inoffensively remind you that where a COLD, a COUGH, or a SORE THROAT interferes with your bodily comfort... you can obtain certain relief through...," etc.

Gargling Oil, Drs. Jayne and Ayer—all the patent-medicine "greats"—used trade cards liberally. Cards which are often charming period pieces still turn up today. They are vivid reminders of the turn of sentiment, the tools, home furnishings, cultural environment, and medications of the nineteenth century.

There is, in a parody of *Patience,* a hint that the advertising cards may have become as much a nuisance to the pharmacist of seventy or eighty years ago as the stamp-buyer of today:

"Major is the name of this *pure blood* Newfoundland dog, [once] owned by the proprietor of Vegetine," the blood medicine which gave humans *pure blood.* The Vegetine man commissioned an artist to paint his pet in oil, the portrait "taken from life" and lithographed to make an ad. Major is—or, alas, *was*—"six years old, weigh[ed] 125 pounds . . . a good watch-dog, and a great pet among children"; he enjoyed playing hide-and-seek or sharing an exciting game of croquet with the young folks. Vegetine was recommended for all diseases of the skin and just about everything else.

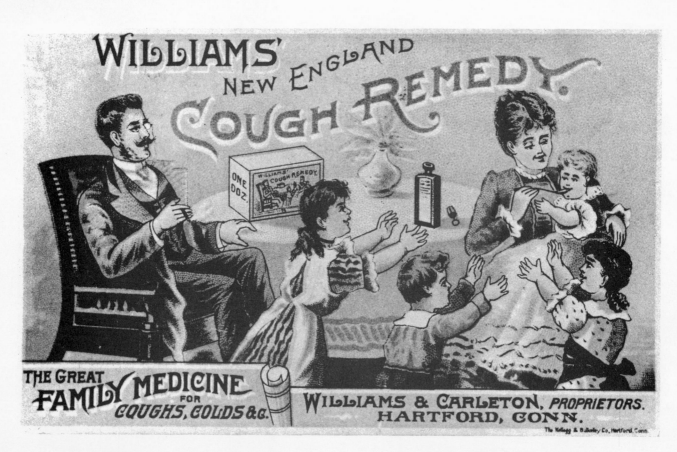

The artist who sketched this pretty scene was well schooled in the tradition of the picture of domestic felicity. But here he had to make the commercial point abundantly—indeed, redundantly—clear. So the anecdotal picture hits bottom, as the wholesome American family gathers around the table and uncorks the cough remedy, the children reaching out eager hands for their daily shot of opiate.

"You must never take it hard if 'Mister,
    got a pikcha card?'
Is heard five hundred times a day."

One can easily imagine the power that was at
work as a family poured over the medicine cards
under the yellow light of the hanging lamp, and
Mother wondered, as she carefully pasted a specimen
in her album, how the advertiser could have hit upon
her distemper so exactly.

The owners of nostrums were well aware
of the fact that the child of today is the
hypochrondiac of tomorrow. Hence many
fetching pictures were created, aimed at
catching the fancy of the little consumers-
in-training.

A note of good-natured satire frequently appeared in the
trade card illustrations. Here the aesthetic movement
and finicky gentility of the upper-middle class gets a
going-over.

You've seen ship models enclosed in a bottle; but did you
ever see a mouse in a bottle? Another life saved by

Pond's Extract, indeed! Note the mouse's immemorial
gesture of contempt toward his frustrated enemies.

corn, *n, slang.* as in corny, *a.* Corn...is sentiment, sincere, and unashamed; corn is the familiar, the tried, and the true.
—*Dictionary of Americanisms,* I, 395.

"Hold your horses!" If you think the traffic accident came in with the automobile—*regardez*, and back-date your ideas. The "runaway" horse and the hero who stopped it are figures in fact as well as fiction. The store interior is saturated with Ayer advertising. The old "show globes" are an authentic touch, as well as the pile of free almanacs on the counter.

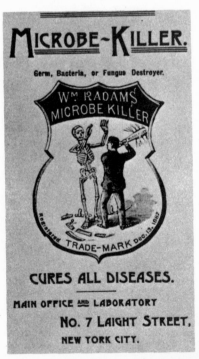

"Twenty years ago," Samuel Hopkins Adams wrote in 1905, "the microbe was making a great stir in the land." Enter, therefore, William Radam and his mighty killer. Then microbes were succeeded by bacteria; and down from Canada came tales of a wonderful new germicide, Powley's Liquified Ozone. Moved to Chicago, rechristened Liquozone, this weak solution of acids in hydrant water did so well that when sugaring-off time came, the *net* profits for the first fiscal year were $1,800,000.

IN THE WAKE OF THE NEWS

The advertisements published by the patents were often topical to a high degree, seizing upon the events which shook and moved the people. Science, invention, public affairs, prominent personalities are given a timely whirl. The same alertness is reflected in the trade names too—Electric Bitters, Telephone Headache Tablets, Radam's Microbe Killer, Edison's Polyform, Garfield Tea.

When James G. Blaine was the "plumed knight" of Republican politics, Hood's Sarsaparilla associated itself with Blaine by publishing a thumbnail biography. When the big event was the World's Columbian Exposition in Chicago, Syrup of Figs was there, and Ayer and—remember?—Clark Stanley, the Rattlesnake King. When Theodore Roosevelt sent the "Great White Fleet" around the world, Perry Davis' Pain Killer recorded the event in a souvenir brochure. Medical science had no sooner entered into new, fruitful investigations of the glands of internal secretion than the Capricorn Chemical Company came up with Goat Lymph Tablets.

Here, and on the following pages, are a few instances of how the proprietary ads reflected their particular moment in time.

The very early Santa Claus shown is quite near to the German St. Nicholas. The details of his costume are particularly interesting because they give us the Christmas saint in transition—before he had become conventionalized into the modern Santa. Dancer, Prancer, et al., are bringing a bottle of cherry pectoral. Just what the whole family wanted!

111

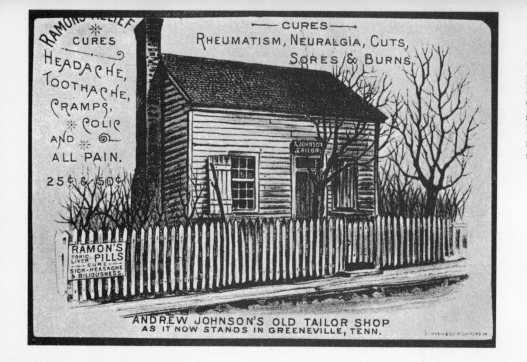

In 1875 Andrew Johnson returned to the U.S. Senate after his near impeachment as President of the United States. Here a fellow townsman of Greenville, Tennessee, Ramon's Pepsin Headache Cure, Relief and Liver Pills celebrates appropriately the early rise and later vindication of the former tailor's apprentice.

When Columbus made a landfall in the Western Hemisphere, the first thing that met his eyes was a gigantic sign saying "Ayer's Sarsaparilla," according to the J. C. Ayer Company. Similarly, Mrs. Pinkham associated herself with the greatest engineering marvel of the patent-medicine age—the Brooklyn Bridge.

This might be the proscenium and curtain of almost any small-town opera house where the patrons hissed the villain and wept as the soubrette sang "The Pardon Came Too Late." In reality the curtain was surrounded by local ads for the meat market, livery stable, barbershop, milliner (who was said to be "fast"), and the racket store.

GREATEST DISCOVERIES
OF THE 19TH CENTURY

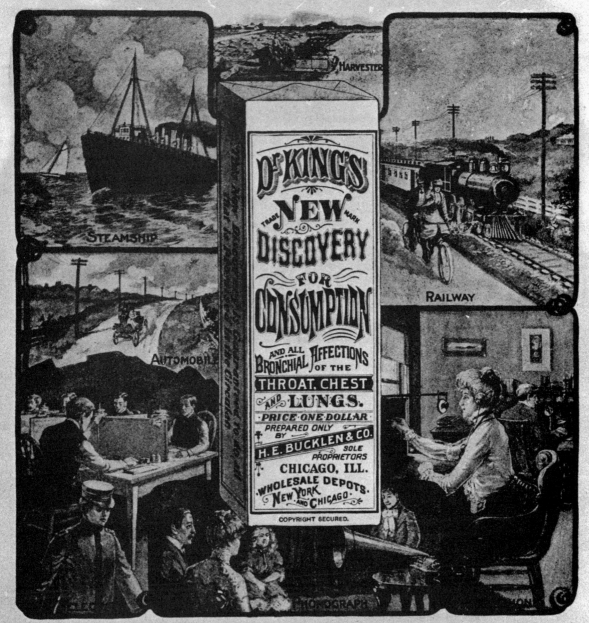

DR. KING'S NEW DISCOVERY
THE GREATEST OF ALL
FOR SAVING HUMAN LIFE

What were the people excited about as they looked back at the marvels of science around the turn of the century? Dr. King gives the honors to the steamship, the railway, the telephone, the phonograph, the telegraph, and the automobile—up to a point. But overtopping all was the breakthrough in preventive medicine—the New Discovery for Consumption and all Bronchial Affections of the Throat, Chest, and Lungs.

The First Hundred Years Were the Hardest

Probably the best-known painting by a U. S. artist and a striking popular success of the art exhibit at the Philadelphia Centennial Exposition of 1876 was the painting by Archibald M. Willard known at the time as *Yankee Doodle,* later more reverently as the *Spirit of '76.* It told a people in retrospective mood what they wished to believe about the origins of the hundred years of liberty they were celebrating. Reproduced literally millions of times in books, magazines, histories, and on calendars, the picture was also freely adapted and used in advertising, as in the harness-oil advertisement shown here. The other versions are of course crude burlesques of the Willard canvas. The second picture from the top is a stock trade card in blank, never imprinted.

Willard, a decorator of farm and circus wagons, and, like Cassily Adams, absent from the biographical dictionaries of American artists, produced a picture at which the Centennial crowds gazed with deep emotion. It was a human document. Curiously enough, the original idea for the picture was humorous. It was planned to be a good-natured jibe at a Fourth of July celebration in a sleepy country village. Willard had observed many such occasions in his home town of Wellington, Ohio. A Cleveland art dealer persuaded the painter to switch the conception to the serious patriotic theme. The rest is history, or at least graphic folklore.

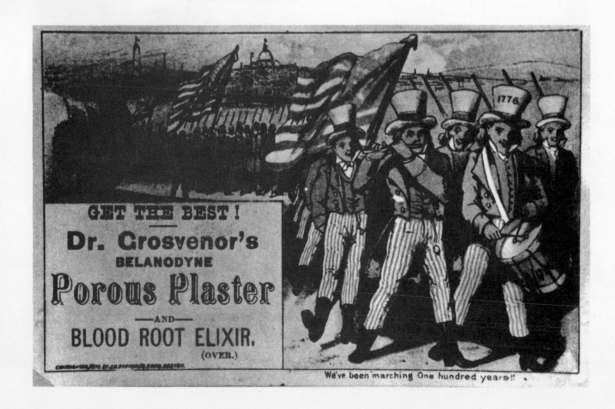

We've been marching One hundred years!!

Monkey Business

The theory of organic evolution advanced a hundred years ago by Charles Darwin, and expanded into a theory of society by Herbert Spencer, raised a storm in the United States as science and theology met in a head-on collision. Lecturers and preachers debated the great issues involved. The Reverend Charles Hodge, biblical scholar and ardent anti-evolutionist, asserted with satisfaction that in all his fifty years in office not a new idea had come out of Princeton. "Natural selection" and "acquired and inherited traits" became cant phrases of the day, invoked in all sorts of connections. "Survival of the fittest," applied to business as well as biology, was "merely the working-out of a law of nature and a law of God," John D. Rockefeller told a Sunday-school class. The pangs, the wounds, and the anguish of the struggle over whether man was made in God's image, or was simply a smart ape, percolated down through all strata of society, finally reaching the patent-medicine public in dilute form. In the puzzle card below, astrology and Darwin's great contribution to biological thought provide amusement for an idle hour, "and thus settle the ancestral question a la Darwin."

Around the World in Seventy-Two Days, or, the Female Phileas Fogg

Jules Verne's best seller of the 1870s, *Around the World in Eighty Days,* and its fictional hero, Phileas Fogg, had a counterpart in real life.

Young, pretty, and indubitably a lady, Elizabeth Cochrane announced in 1889 that she would try to beat the imaginary Fogg's time—and she did it. Elizabeth started from Jersey City, New Jersey, on November 14, at nine hours, forty minutes, and six seconds, with the blessing and backing of Joseph Pulitzer's New York *World.* The dash caught the imagination of the whole world. Everyone knew Elizabeth by her professional name, Nellie Bly, the first New York newspaperwoman; and by her "trademark" costume—a sensible but becoming dress of blue broadcloth, with bustle, bones and all, a camel's hair coat, double-peaked gillie cap, satchel, and two watches. The girl, the costume, and the journey made history. There were Nellie Bly games, Nellie Bly poetry, Nellie Bly dresses, endorsements of bank checks, face powder, corsets, luggage, and the Nellie Bly Self-Wringing Mop. Nellie's face became almost as well known as that of Lydia E. Pinkham, and the lyrics of a song in the operetta *The Black Hussar* included:

"I wonder when they'll send a girl
To travel round the sky,
Read the answer in the stars,
They wait for Nellie Bly."

Nellie got caught up in the glamour of the plugola world, and before she was through, she had endorsed La Cigale Tobacco and *two* patent medicines—Dr. Morse's remedies and Dr. Schenck's Mandrake Pills. Schenck is the man of whom a biographer wrote a few years before the Nellie Bly tie-in: "The doctor makes no pretensions to extraordinary medical knowledge. He is not college-bred, he don't carry a big-headed stick, nor bridge his nose with gold spectacles to give him a wise look, nor does he cough and cry 'Hem!' nor make use of Latin phrases, nor affect the Sir Oracle in any manner or form."

Schenck simply appeared out of Trenton as a young man bearing a banner with a strange device— "Consumption Can Be Cured"—and in the course of a long life acquired "a reputation that is worth more than silver and gold or precious stones."

But, for his labors, Dr. Schenck acquired those baubles too.

NELLIE BLY, ON THE FLY.

When Nellie Bly went on the fly,
To show what courage dared to try,
She made the startled world contess:
Men don't monopolize success.

Schenck's Mandrake Pills

FOLLOW
THE LEADER

The early patent-medicine advertising divertisements combined seed-catalogue mendacity with Chamber of Commerce enthusiasm, and perfected the appeal to outside authority to bear witness to the tale. The nostrums made testimonial advertising what it is today, a powerful if controversial method for attracting attention and building confidence. The recommendations from grateful customers who believed that they had been saved in the nick of time were the foundation stones of any proprietary business. They were easy to acquire. One sure way for a man to see his name in the papers was to rent out his sluggish colon to a medicine firm.

The letters from plasterers, railroad firemen, housewives, and old Army veterans were usually authentic documents, perhaps puffed up a bit by the advertising department; but they were sincere. That is, the writer believed what he said, even if he didn't know what he was talking about. This was the central fallacy: that the medicine-taker could diagnose his own troubles, administer the medicine, and interpret the results. And quite often prominent persons were lured or trapped into issuing statements which they were not qualified to make.

In cases of minor or chronic conditions, the

One of the oldest advertising schemes is the theatrical plug: both parties can use the publicity. Lillian Russell spoke for Carboline. Julia Marlowe took her cocktails in the form of Peruna. Sarah Bernhardt, the Divine Sarah, approved of both Duffy's Pure Malt Whiskey and Paine's Celery Compound, an alcoholic nostrum that died with Repeal, along with Pinelyptus Pastilles and other preparations of equal therapeutic insignificance.

Below: from the files of *The Journal of the American Medical Association.*

LETTERS FOR RENT

300,000 Jas. Wm. Kidd medical file cards, representing all kinds of diseases (will sort) 1904.
180,000 men's matrimonial, 35,000 women's '04, 1st.
200,000 agents and canvassers.
50,000 Dr. Pierce order blanks, '02, '03.
20,000 Ozomulson order blanks, '03.
30,280 Theo. Noel, '02, '03, medical file cards.
59,000 Agents' directory, '03, '04, '05.
250,000 Home work, '03, '04, '05.
27,500 Rosebud trust, firsts, '03, '04.
19,500 Bond Jewelry payups, trust. '04, envelopes.
52,000 10c song orders, Star Music Co., '04, '05.
17,500 Dr. May & Friar. ladies' regulator. '03, '04.
6,000 Nervous debility, '03, '04, Appliance Co.
Over 1,000,000 letters on hand, all kinds. Call or write me for samples and ads. Letters bought.
C. A. Davis, 1634 W. Ohio Street, Chicago.

Most of the anxious correspondents who wrote in confidence to patent-medicine concerns were bucolic individuals who lived in the kind of town where attending funerals was a major recreation. The letters from sick people were a valuable commodity. When they had been milked of their first-run value, it was the custom of the trade to sell, exchange, or rent them. Brokers would quote a prospective buyer, giving quantity and price on, say, asthma letters, deaf letters, or stomach-trouble letters—or simply "300,000 Dr. Jas. Wm. Kidd, medical file cards, all diseases, will sort."

A Posthumous Testimonial

ROCHESTER DEMOCRAT AND CHRONICLE.

JUNE 20, 1930   JUNE 25, 1930

JAMES KIMBER, ONCE ALDERMAN IS DEAD AT 62

Came to Rochester 45 Years Ago and Entered Service of Central Road

James R. Kimber, former alderman of the Twenty-first Ward and prominent Mason, died suddenly yesterday at his home, 314 Winton Road North, aged 62 years. Mr. Kimber had been in poor health for several months, but had been at work as usual and news of his death came as a shock to his friends.

Mr. Kimber served as alderman of the Twenty-first Ward for two terms, going out of office when City Manager Charter went into effect, Jan. 1, 1928. He with the City Manager working for the new charter and

LABOR OFFICIAL PRAISES SARGON FOR NEW HEALTH

Regained 18 Lbs. of Lost Weight and Troubles Disappeared, Says Kimber

"I've gained eighteen pounds in about six weeks' time", enthusiastically declared Jas. R. Kimber, 314 Winton Rd., Rochester, recently in relating his experience with Sargon. Mr. Kimber is connected

JAS. R. KIMBER

with the N. Y. C. R. R., and is one of the most prominent Masons in the state.

"I'd been having terrible headaches and bilious spells and I felt so upset at times I could hardly keep anything on my stomach. Constipation bothered me continually, and then a rheumatic condition set in. I was weak and nervous, didn't sleep well, and I lost weight rapidly.

"I felt myself gaining ground right from the first few doses of Sargon; as I 'snapped out' of my troubles I gradually got back my weight, and the feeling of strength

Sargon is another of the highly (18 per cent) alcoholic nostrums. It was put on the market by the man who made Tanlac (also 18 per cent alcohol) famous. Like its prototype, it is introduced by heavy advertising, mostly of the testimonial type. Its most powerful ingredient furnishes the repeat element. The Rochester (N. Y.) *Democrat and Chronicle* of June 20, 1930, recorded the death of Mr. James R. Kimber. *Five days later the same*

patient might live for years, sampling the merits of various cures and filing his opinion of their merits in the archives of the manufacturers, already crammed with such medical and literary curiosities. More serious, and definitely embarrassing, was the situation when the endorser inconsiderately died before his testimonial was published. Such was the contretemps that faced the Konjola man who was demonstrating Konjola at the Brown-Jones Cut Rate Drug Store in Meadville, Pennsylvania. And at the same time Mr. Addison R. Sheckler was saying in the local newspaper, "Konjola Put Me Back on the Job, and I Feel Like a Different Person," while the Konjola concern gloated, "Another Victory for Konjola." But Sheckler, alas—Sheckler was dead and had been three weeks in his grave at the time.

A variant form of testimonial was to give a newsy effect by sending out newspaper advertisements with instructions to "insert name of your city in heading of each ad." Thus the apparently local item would appear identically as AUSTIN RESIDENT HAS AWFUL EXPERIENCE, HORNELL RESIDENT HAS AWFUL EXPERIENCE, MARION RESIDENT . . . , and so on. But it was the same old resident, regardless of what newspaper you read. And the resident wasn't local.

Public figures were given a rough time of it by the gee-whiz industry. When the former Frances Folsom became Mrs. Grover Cleveland, bells rang, cannon boomed, and Sulphur Bitters honored her with an ad (right). President Harrison's portrait was appropriated by Dr. Harter's Little Liver Pills, St.

Mrs. President Cleveland.

Jacob's Oil, and Warner's Safe Cure. Thomas A. Edison and Whitelaw Reid appeared for Siegel's Syrup and General Grant for Tolu Rock and Rye.

Below is an example of the "reverend dodge." These distinguished divines gave the patient looking for a potable medicine full license to drink whisky for the stomach's sake. Durham ran a matrimonial bureau in Wyoming. Houghton was a Deputy Internal Revenue Collector and followed the horses. McLeod labored in his pastorate at Greenleaf, Michigan (pop. 893).

IT PAYS TO ADVERTISE

The "American system" of mass production could have made little stir in the world if the new industries had not been able to distribute consumer goods to a national market. Transportation was needed, and mass communications and a transfer of the control of distribution from the small merchant to the large manufacturer. Otherwise the benefits of machine production would not have been realized. It is a thing to marvel at, that the pieces in this complex puzzle all fell into place at about the same time. The railroad network was completed; postal rates fell; a new popular newspaper and periodical press came alive.

The patent-medicine makers demonstrated at the same time the power of brand-name merchandising. They created the public image of a trade-mark by using ideas, pictures, slogans, and mnemonic devices to establish a product personality; as when Barker's liniment adapted freely the first line of the first verse of a famous old hymn to sing "Joy to the World, Relief Has Come"; as when Doan's Kidney Pills dramatized

WHAT THE GOVERNORS SAID

SAID THE GOVERNOR OF NEW YORK, TO THE GOVERNOR OF MASSACHUSETTS IN ORDER BENJAMIN, TO HAVE A PURE GOVERNMENT WE MUST PURIFY THE PEOPLE

SAID THE GOVERNOR OF MASSACHUSETTS TO THE GOVERNOR OF NEW YORK, RIGHT YOU ARE GROVER, AND THIS IS THE PURIFIER THAT WILL DO IT HOOD'S SARSAPARILLA.

C. I. Hood & Company is making a sly adaptation, for its own purposes, of the widespread belief that what the governor of South Carolina said to the governor of North Carolina was, "It's a long time between drinks."

pictorially the idea that a pain in the lower lumbar region means the old kidney is kicking up. The gesture came to trigger a reflex action—"Get Doan's."

At one time newspapers placed restrictions on the use of display type in advertisements. The advertisers used repetition and white space to circumvent the publishers. Thus:

H. H. Warner is credited with inventing the paid advertisement dressed up as a local news story, and there were many who followed his lead. As below:

Old Subscriber would open his favorite country gazette and start in on an account of the local political scene, and before he knew it he was in the iron embrace of somebody's Pleasant Pellets.

The roll of the seasons, the seasons of the calendar and of human life, were recorded faithfully by the pill-rollers. Advent brought the new stock of almanacs. Spring was marked by an outbreak of symptoms of a vague but endemic disease called "spring fever," which required a course of medicine to "thin" the blood. Versatile Plantation Bitters was good for this. It was also efficacious as a "summer restorative," a "fall medicine," and a "winter stimulant." Tarrant's Effervescent Seltzer Aperient had the same built-in, all-weather efficiency.

A sure sign of spring, around turnip-green time,

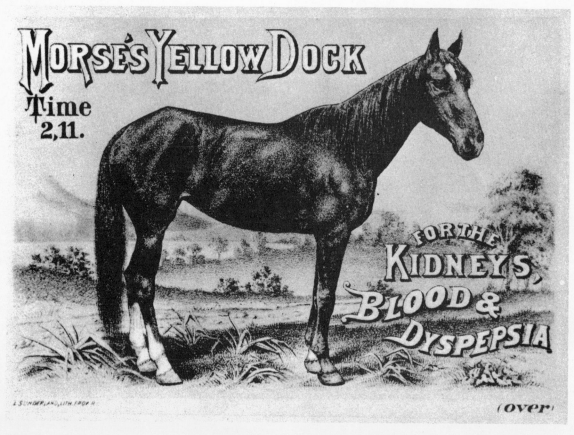

Victims of biliousness, dizziness, and general debility who followed the horses must have been loyal to the Morse Yellow Dock Root Company of Providence, Rhode Island, because the handsome chestnut mare shown above "is our advertising medium for their Great Remedy—Morse's Yellow Dock." The mare stood 15-3 high, with three white feet and a star on her forehead. She weighed one thousand pounds, was seven years old, perfectly sound, without a blemish. She was sired by Clark's Mohawk, Jr., dammed by a copperbottom mare, and scored with the fastest record ever made at Narragansett Park up to November 3, 1882—namely, 2:11.

was the appearance of the patent-medicine salesman, slogging along hub deep on muddy roads, tacking bright signs as he went, on barns, trees, store fronts, telegraph poles—even homes, if you didn't watch out —flashing once again the names of Black Draught, Kodol, Grove's, or King of Malaria. Spring was the time when a farmer could get his barn painted free. But the paint job included, he found, some gigantic letters which he hadn't bargained for—HOOD'S, ONLY HOOD'S. He could go on from there, if he had a mind to, and get his roof painted too, with AYER'S SARSAPARILLA—ALWAYS ON TOP.

Another harbinger of spring was the free medicine sample. Local juvenile delinquents, equipped with stout canvas bags, padded along wooden sidewalks with catlike tread, to toss panacea circulars wrapped around sample packages of Garfield Tea and Dr. Carter's K. and B. Tea on front porches. The lady of the house, if she brewed the gift under the supposition that it was simply tea, was shortly due for a rude surprise.

Once one ventured out into the world, it was evident that the medicine adman had been there first, the board-fence bill posters and the rock painters, the curbstone artists and the sidewalk stencilers. Ads appeared on the risers of the steps leading up to the New York elevated-railway stations. Blaring notices in white and yellow paint covered every fence and wall,

in praise of liniments, aperients, plasters, powders, and hair dyes. A man taking a horse car downtown in New York had the impression, "We breakfast on aloes, dine on quassia, sup on logwood and myrrh, and sleep on morphine and prussic acid."

Anything that had a smooth surface, that rose above the ground between New York and Philadelphia and could be seen from the train, was decorated with the name of Dr. J. A. Schenck. The view up the Hudson River was enlivened by Carboline, Tarrant's Aperient, and Gargling Oil. Leaving Albany, Vinegar Bitters took over. St. Jacob's Oil was the feature many newlyweds remembered from their visit to Niagara Falls, while Chicago was "the paradise of whitepaint-ism," one traveler noted, "with a splendid exhibition of medical and chemical notices." The gorges of the Rockies vibrated with bright frescoes for tonics and laxatives. And on the rocks of the Mississippi bluffs, near Alton, Illinois, where Father Marquette had seen a primitive painting of unknown provenance called the *Piasa Bird* Francis Parkman saw, "instead of Marquette's monsters . . . a huge advertisement of 'Plantation Bitters.'"

"What is this strange power?" the midway barker used to ask rhetorically, holding up the bottle on high. But the power wasn't in the bottle. It was in the advertising—American evangelism applied to material things.

What is it? The exact nature of this object of wood and wire, shaped like a lyre, is uncertain. But it was probably a form of retail-store advertising for the famous Pink Pills for Pale People, to be mounted on the door of the store. When a customer entered, the metal balls swung outward and back, sounding a musical chord—the dominant seventh, no doubt.

121

Fig 1. Demon of Catarrh. Fig 2. Demon of Neuralgia. Fig 3. Demon of Headache Fig 4. Demon of Weak Nerves. Fig 5.5 Demons of Toothache.

122

Many proprietary manufacturers tried their hand over the years at delineating graphically the ills which beset man—to catch in line and wash the very "demon" of some common illness, often with nightmarish results. Wolcott's little monsters, numbered from one to five, seem to win the horror sweepstakes!

Tireless... on Their Appointed Rounds

THIS TEAM HAS BEEN ON THE ROAD ADVERTISING.

The medicine peddler competed with the clock merchant and other itinerants in the rural barter trade for farm chickens, eggs, and goose feathers. New England folklore records the encounter of a medicine hawker and a tombstone salesman at a narrow bridge. "After you," said the mortuary gentleman, stepping aside courteously.

Any rock that didn't shout "Plymouth Rock Pants" was sure to be embellished with the name of Wizard or Gargling Oil—white or yellow on a black background. There was an old New England saying to the effect that if a man "gets up March hill," he is good for all summer. Thus he escaped for another year the dread malady known as "forty years' consumption," which often caught up with its victims just when they were getting ready to celebrate their one hundredth birthday.

Charles A. Vogeler of Baltimore was a gifted promoter who acquired the formula for an ointment while attending a German university. The result was St. Jacob's Oil. One stunt of Vogeler's was to operate a steamboat on the Ohio and Mississippi rivers to distribute printed matter to the shanty people and to the inhabitants of the river towns, booming the Great German Remedy. The steamer was painted a brilliant red, with "St. Jacob's Oil" on the sides in twelve-foot lettering. The saloon was frescoed and gilded in the Eastlake style, furnished with a Turkish carpet, Queen Anne furniture, damask curtains, the finest silver, china, and table linen.

123

LOUISIANA HAYRIDE

The greatest medicine-show extravaganza ever seen in the United States played to Standing Room Only, not one hundred years ago, not fifty years ago, not twenty-five years ago, but right in the last decade, when a smart country boy from the "Evangeline country" of Louisiana parlayed a dietary supplement of vitamins, minerals, honey, and firewater into a business that could budget $15,000,000 for advertising in a single year. When it was called to the attention of home-grown, go-getting Senator Dudley Joseph Le-Blanc, President, Vice-President, Secretary, Treasurer, and Chairman of the Board of The LeBlanc Corporation that the Illinois legislature had adopted a resolution urging that he quit using child testimonials, and that the upper-class Chicago suburb of Northbrook was considering banning his merchandise altogether, bottle and jug, LeBlanc was unruffled.

"That's the price of success, son," he said. "I'm the next governor, boy." He meant Louisiana, not Illinois.

What was LeBlanc's composition, Hadacol, good

The advertisement above, the subject of wide notoriety and comment, is typical of the razzle-dazzle schemes which the father of Hadacol cooked up to attract attention to his murky brown mixture. Senator LeBlanc probably never expected to see a parrot so gifted. But Barnum would have understood, and approved.

for? Groucho Marx once asked this question of the medical Santa Claus on a television show.

"Hadacol," replied its pappy, in a flash of misunderstanding, "was good for five million dollars last year."

The package itself was cautious, vague, and yet wildly inclusive in what it claimed for the preparation. In substance, if Hadacol was what you needed, it was what you needed.

A sassy, brash extrovert, LeBlanc was born into a large Cajun family. He started out as a pants presser, progressed to tacking up Bull Durham signs, promoted a burial-insurance scheme, worked for a while for a patent-medicine company. He quit because his mother taught him always to be honest. But the urge to go into business for himself was too strong to be denied. Le-Blanc found himself with a little proprietary article of his own, Happy Day Headache Powder. Happy Day didn't accomplish what Dud had in mind. Neither did his Dixie Dew Cough Remedy.

A personal bout with arthritis led the senator (state, not U.S.) to his stroke of genius, Hadacol—the name derived from the first syllables of Happy Day Company, plus "l" from LeBlanc. "Haddy*col*," its creator called it, with the accent on the last syllable. For five years, brown, fishy-smelling Haddy*col* was little more than a local nostrum. Then "Couzain Dud" —everbody is cousin in Cajun country—got a line of credit for twenty days' advertising from some newspapers. Sales began to roll. LeBlanc threw everything on the board, pyramided over and over again. In 1950 the zany Hadacol medicine show went on the road. The Hadacol Good Will Caravan consisted of a fleet of white and blue trucks, Dixieland bands, Hollywood entertainers such as Mickey Rooney, Chico Marx, Burns and Allen, Carmen Miranda. There were souvenirs too—cowboy regalia, squirt pistols, balloons and bubble gum, Hadacol caps and T shirts for the teen-

Dudley J. LeBlanc didn't claim to be a doctor. He was just a boy from the Deep South who could sell anything. But he projected a conception of himself as The People's Benefactor. When General MacArthur returned from the Far East, trailing clouds of glory, LeBlanc promptly offered him $150,000 a year to come to Lafayette, Louisiana, and be Vice-President. Another stunt—the senator announced that one thousand carrier pigeons would compete in flying Hadacol orders from drug distributors to Lafayette. The winner was to get a life annuity of choice pigeon feed and "a beautiful lady pigeon for a girl friend."

Showman LeBlanc rehearsing in a Chicago hotel room with part of his star-spangled cast for the opening of a Box Top Rally. Self-styled friend of man, especially of old men, LeBlanc claimed that he was the direct descendant of the notary in Longfellow's poem *Evangeline*.

agers. The ticket of admission to the show was one Hadacol box top, cheap enough for a sight of Buglin' Sam, two calliopes, and a chorus line from the Chez Paree in Chicago. There were other elaborations of the theme; a well-stacked Hadacol queen, Hadacol credit cards, a Captain Hadacol comic strip. Juke boxes blared out the "Hadacol Boogie." New Orleans had a niterie, the Hadacol Club. Dud publicized printable jokes to supplement *sub rosa* rumors that Haddy*col* had extraordinary powers as an aphrodisiac. At Southern football games, the rooters yelled "Give him Hadacol." A Louisiana soft-drink bottler tried to hang onto two coattails at once by bringing out Hadacola. LaBlanc was willing, but the Coca-Cola people, having already defended their melodious syllables some two thousand times against such improprieties as Hava-Cola, Kola Koke, including a cigarette called Smoka-Cola, nipped Hadacola in the bud.

Meanwhile Couzain Dud rode around in a new Cadillac. "Got rid of the old one," he explained. "The ash trays got full." Dud liked to stop on impulse at roadside taverns and present lipsticks to the waitresses, accompanied by a few gallantries. What the spellbinder of the bayous sold was not vitamins and minerals or even the equivalent of a dry martini. No, it was something different; there was a dream in every bottle: "Hadacol for a better tomorrow." Yet nothing fades faster than a dream, unless it is a fad, especially one that is undercapitalized. In 1951 the senator sold his elixir to two New York attorneys. A product of the same name is now being marketed by a company under different management.

Bibliography

This is a selective list of materials consulted. Books cited in the text and standard reference works have been omitted.

BOOKS

Adams, George Worthington. *Doctors in Blue.* New York, 1952.

Adams, Samuel Hopkins. *Grandfather Stories.* New York, 1955.

———. *The Great American Fraud.* New York, c. 1906.

Atherton, Lewis. *Main Street on the Middle Border.* Bloomington, Ind., 1954.

Baker, Nina Brown. *Nellie Bly.* New York, 1956.

Bingay, Malcolm W. *Of Me I Sing.* Indianapolis, 1949.

Biographical Review of Calhoun County. Chicago, 1904.

Briante, Dr. John Goodale. *The Old Root and Herb Doctor, or the Indian Method of Healing.* Claremont (N.H.), 1870.

Buley, R. Carlyle. *The Old Northwest. Pioneer Period. 1815–1840.* 2 vols. Indianapolis, 1950.

Carson, Gerald. *The Old Country Store.* New York, 1954.

Chase, A. W., M.D., *Dr. Chase's Recipes; or, Information for Everybody.* Ann Arbor (Mich.), 1866.

Clark, Thomas D. *Pills, Petticoats and Plows.* Indianapolis, 1944.

Cook, James. *Remedies and Rackets.* New York, 1958.

Crabtree, A. D. *The Funny Side of Physic.* Hartford: (Conn.), 1874.

Cramp, Arthur J., M.D. *Nostrums and Quackery.* 3 vols. Chicago, 1912, 1921, 1936.

Daring Donald McKay, or, The Last War Trail of the Modocs. Erie (Penna.), 1887.

Gifford, Sanford K. *Garlic and Old Horse Blankets.* Chicago, 1943.

Hall, Henry. Ed., *American Successful Men of Affairs.* 2 vols. New York, 1896.

Holbrook, Stewart H. *The Golden Age of Quackery.* New York, 1959.

Hopkins, Claude C. *My Life in Advertising.* New York, 1927.

Hornung, Clarence P. *Handbook of Early American Advertising Art.* New York, 1953.

Hoyt, Harlowe R. *Town Hall Tonight.* Englewood Cliffs (N.J.), 1955.

Marshall, W. G. *Through America, or, Nine Months in the United States.* London, 1881.

McKelvey, Blake. *Rochester: The Flower City, 1855–90.* Cambridge, 1949.

McNeal, Violet. *Four White Horses and a Brass Band.* Garden City, N.Y., 1947.

Men Who Advertise, The, New York, 1870.

Oleson, Charles W. *Secret Nostrums and Systems of Medicine. A Book of Formulas.* Chicago, 1899.

Picard, Madge E., and Buley, R. Carlyle. *The Midwest Pioneer, His Ills, Cures, & Doctors.* New York, 1946.

Pierce, R. V., M.D. *The People's Common Sense Medical Adviser.* Buffalo (N.Y.), 1918.

Presbrey, Frank. *The History and Development of Advertising.* Garden City, N.Y., 1929.

Ratner, Sidney. *New Light on the History of Great American Fortunes. American Millionaires of 1892 and 1902.* New York, 1953.

Rowell, George Presbury. *Forty Years An Advertising Agent.* New York, 1906.

Sullivan, Mark. *Our Times.* Vol. 2. New York, 1927.

Washburn, Robert Collyer. *The Life and Times of Lydia E. Pinkham.* New York, 1931.

PERIODICALS

Shryock, Richard H. "The Significance of Medicine in American History." *American Historical Review.* LXII. No. 1. October 1956.

LeBlanc, Thomas J. "The Medicine Show." *The American Mercury.* Vol 5. No. 18. June 1925.

Gunning, Robert, "Hypocrite's Highball." *Ibid.* December 1942.

Billboard. Various dates, 1915–30.

Dykstra, David L. "The Medical Profession and Patent and Proprietary Medicines During the Nineteenth Century." *Bulletin of the History of Medicine.* XXIX. No. 5. September–October, 1955.

Bulletin of Pharmacy. Various dates, 1905–06.

Young, James Harvey, and Griffenhagen, George B. "Old English Patent Medicines in America." *The Chemist and Druggist.* June 29, 1957.

Young, James Harvey. "The Origin of Patent Medicines in America." *The Chemist and Druggist.* September 9, 1959.

———. "The Hadacol Phenomenon." *The Emory University Quarterly.* June 1951.

"Don't Fall For the Bustline Racket." *Good Housekeeping.* August 1958.

Journal of the American Medical Association. Various dates, 1900–51.

Moore, Mary F. "Advertising Cards of the '80's in Upstate New York." *New York History.* October 1949.

Neisuler, Jeanette. "Medicine in Early Schnectady." *Ibid.* October 1955.

Ratcliffe, J. D. "The Hullabaloo About Hadacol." *Reader's Digest.* July 1951.

Stout, Wesley. "Med Show." *Saturday Evening Post.* September 14, 1929.

———. "Alagazam." *Ibid.* October 19, 1929.

"Proprietary Specialties." *Scientific American.* March 26, 1881.

Young, James Harvey. "Patent Medicines in the Early Nineteenth Century." *The South Atlantic Quarterly.* October 1949.

"The Package Medicine Industry." *Standard Remedies.* December 1916.

Strohl, E. Lee, M.D. "Ladies of Lynn—Emphasis on One." *Surgery, Gynecology & Obstetrics.* December 1957.

"From Country Boy to Medicine Magnate." *Tide.* April 13, 1951.

"The Word." *Ibid.* June 29, 1959.

Hebberd, Mary Hardgrove. "Notes on Dr. David Franklin Powell, Known as 'White Beaver.'" *Wisconsin Magazine of History.* Summer 1952.

NEWSPAPERS

Scattered issues of many newspapers were consulted, especially for obituary articles summarizing the careers of various manufacturers of proprietaries, among them:

Gilbert, Douglas. "Spring Brings Out the Spielers and the Sap." New York *World-Telegram.* April 21, 22, 23, 1947.

"Essa and Gay Billings, Show Folks For Half Century." Quincy (Ill.) *Herald-Whig.* January 15, 1950.

Merrill, Arch. "The Seven Sisters With the Longest Hair in the World." Rochester *Democrat and Chronicle.* June 8, 1952.

———. "Even the Sutherland Sisters' Funerals Were Spectacular." *Ibid.* June 15, 1952.

———. "Showplace of the Countryside Was the Seven Sisters' Mansion." *Ibid.* June 22, 1952.

Wilford, John H. "Old-Time Remedies." *Wall Street Journal.* October 9, 1959.

PAMPHLETS

Consumption Cures, Cough Remedies, etc. Chicago, n.d.

Cullen, Frederick, J., M.D. *Inside the Home Medicine Chest.* Washington (D.C.), 1951; and (revised) 1960.

Electricity, Nature's Chief Restorer. Pulvermacher's *Electric Belts, Etc.* Cincinnati, n.d.

Female Weakness Cures. Chicago, 1937.

German Electric Belts and Appliances, The, Brooklyn (N.Y.), n.d.

Gift For Young and Old, A., St. Jacob's Oil. Baltimore, 1879.

Grinnell, Ashbel P., M.D. *A Review of Drug Consumption and Alcohol as Found in Proprietary Medicines.* New York, c. 1905.

Ke-ne-o-tah, or the Indian Squaw of the Mohawks. New York, c. 1880.

Nostrums For Kidney Diseases and Diabetes. Chicago, 1923.

McElree, Rev., R. L. *Home Treatment of Female Diseases.* Chattanooga (Tenn.), 1894.

Mechanical Nostrums and Quackery of the Drugless Type. Chicago, 1923.

Medical Mail Order Concerns. Chicago, 1924.

Miscellaneous Nostrums. Chicago, 1923.

Miscellaneous "Specialists." Chicago, n.d.

"Obesity Cures." Chicago, n.d.

Testimonials. Chicago, n.d.

GOVERNMENT PUBLICATIONS

Census Reports. Vol. VII. Twelfth Census of the United States, Taken in the Year 1900. *Manufactures. Part I. United States by Industries.* Washington (D.C.), 1902.

Connecticut Experiment Station Report. Proprietaries. 1912.

Department of the Interior. Office of Indian Affairs. *Circular.* August 10, 1905.

New Hampshire State Board of Health. *New Hampshire Sanitary Bulletin.* April 1907. Quoted in *Journal of the American Medical Association.* June 22, 1907.

Report on Manufacturing Industries in the United States at the Eleventh Census: 1890. Part II. Statistics of Cities. Washington, (D.C.), 1895.

State of Illinois. Illinois State Museum. *Piasa Bird: Fact or Fiction?* Wayne C. Temple. Springfield (Ill.), 1956.

State of Ohio Dairy and Food Department. *Patent or Proprietary Medicines.* Springfield (Ohio), 1910.

Thirteenth Census of the United States, Taken in the Year 1910. Vol. X. *Manufactures, 1909. Reports for Principal Industries.* Washington (D.C.), 1913.

MISCELLANEOUS

Asher & Adams' New Columbian Rail Road Atlas and Pictorial Album of American Industry. New York, 1876.

Drugs. Sears, Roebuck & Company. Chicago, c. 1903.

Van Schaack & Sons, Peter. *Price Current and Illustrated Catalogue, 1887.* Chicago.

Warner's Artist's Album. Rochester (N.Y.), c. 1888.

ALMANACS

Medical almanacs published by various firms were examined, covering the period between 1858 and 1909. They include: *Burdock's Blood Bitters, Dr. John Bull's United States Almanac, Dr. O. Phelps Brown's Shakespearian Annual Almanac, Green's August Flower and German Syrup Almanac, Hostetter's Almanac, Jayne's Medical Almanac and Guide to Health, Kickapoo almanacs, Ladies Birthday Almanac, McLean's Family Almanac, Radway's Ready Relief Almanac, Northwestern Medical Family Almanac, Schenck's Almanac for the Million, Seventh-Day Adventist Family Health Annual* (which might be described as an anti-almanac); *Shaker, Swayne's,* and *Vinegar Bitters* almanacs.

INDEX

Picture Credits

NOTE: Illustrations not otherwise credited are from the author's collection.